THE ULTIMATE
TORONTO BLUE JAYS
TRIVIA BOOK

A Collection of Amazing Trivia Quizzes
and Fun Facts for Die-Hard Blue Jays Fans!

Ray Walker

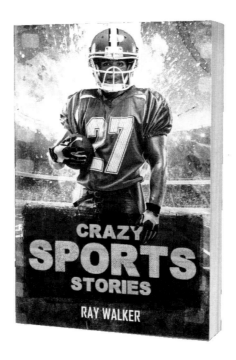

CONTENTS

INTRODUCTION

The Toronto Blue Jays were established in 1977 as an expansion franchise. After the Montreal Expos moved to Washington, DC, and became the Nationals in 2005, the Blue Jays were left as the only Canadian MLB team. Since their founding in the late 1970s, the Blue Jays have proven themselves to be a team that fights hard and is a force to be reckoned with in the MLB postseason.

They currently hold two World Series championships, which they won in the early 1990s. They have also won the American League Pennant twice. They are very often a threat in the American League East Division, having won it six times so far. They also have a wild card berth to their name.

The Blue Jays have retired Roberto Alomar's number as well as the late Roy Halladay's. They also have a "Level of Excellence" at Rogers Centre to celebrate their past and the players and people who made it all possible.

The thing about baseball is that it is a lot like life. There are good times and bad times, good days, and bad days, but you have to do your absolute best to never give up. The Toronto Blue Jays have proven that they refuse to give up and that they will do anything they need to do in order to bring a

1

championship to the city of Toronto and the country of Canada. Winning is more than possible when you have a storied past like the Jays do. They have so much captivating history and so many undeniable player legacies to be profoundly proud of.

The Blue Jays are currently the only MLB team in Canada. They call Rogers Centre home, which opened in 1989 as the SkyDome. They play in arguably the most difficult division in baseball, the American League East, alongside the New York Yankees, Boston Red Sox, Baltimore Orioles, and Tampa Bay Rays.

With such a storied team, you're probably already very knowledgeable as the die-hard Blue Jays fan that you are. Let's test that knowledge to see if you truly are the world's biggest Jays fan.

CHAPTER 1:

ORIGINS & HISTORY

QUIZ TIME!

1. Which of the following team names did the Blue Jays franchise once go by?

    a. Expos

    b. Blues

    c. Raptors

    d. They have always been the Blue Jays

2. In what year was the Toronto Blue Jays franchise established?

    a. 1969

    b. 1977

    c. 1980

    d. 1987

3. The Blue Jays' current home stadium is Rogers Centre.

    a. True

    b. False

4. Which division do the Toronto Blue Jays currently play in?

    a. National League East

    b. American League East

    c. National League West

    d. National League Central

5. The Blue Jays are currently the only MLB team located outside of the United States.

    a. True

    b. False

6. How many American League Pennants has the Blue Jays franchise won (as of the 2019 season)?

    a. 0

    b. 1

    c. 2

    d. 3

7. What is the name of the Blue Jays' mascot?

    a. Ace

    b. Jay

    c. Blue

    d. Birdie

8. Who is the longest-tenured manager in Toronto Blue Jays history (as of 2019 season)?

    a. John Gibbons

    b. Cito Gaston

    c. Bobby Cox

    d. Buck Martinez

9. What is the name of the Toronto Blue Jays' Triple-A farm team and where is it located?

   a. Fresno Grizzlies
   b. Las Vegas Aviators
   c. Omaha Storm Chasers
   d. Buffalo Bisons

10. Who was the first manager of the Blue Jays' franchise?

   a. Harry Warner
   b. Roy Hartsfield
   c. Cookie Rojas
   d. Carlos Tosca

11. As a result of the COVID-19 pandemic, the Blue Jays played their 2020 home season at Sahlen Field in Buffalo, NY.

   a. True
   b. False

12. What is the name of the Blue Jays' current spring training home stadium?

   a. Ed Smith Stadium
   b. First Data Field
   c. TD Ballpark
   d. Hammond Stadium

13. How many appearances has the Toronto Blue Jays franchise made in the MLB playoffs (as of 2019 season)?

   a. 4
   b. 5

c. 7

d. 10

14. How many World Series titles have the Blue Jays won (as of the 2019 season)?

    a. 2

    b. 4

    c. 1

    d. 5

15. The Blue Jays are one of only two MLB teams to be under corporate ownership. The Blue Jays are the only team in the American League to be under corporate ownership.

    a. True

    b. False

16. Which stadium was the first home stadium of the Toronto Blue Jays' franchise?

    a. Toronto Stadium

    b. Sahlen Field

    c. Rogers Centre

    d. Exhibition Stadium

17. As of the 2019 season, how many wild card berths have the Blue Jays won?

    a. 0

    b. 1

    c. 2

    d. 5

18. How many American League East Division titles have the Blue Jays won (as of the 2019 season)?

    a. 4
    b. 6
    c. 8
    d. 10

19. Which team is NOT currently in the American League East Division alongside the Blue Jays?

    a. Baltimore Orioles
    b. New York Yankees
    c. Tampa Bay Rays
    d. Atlanta Braves

20. Out of all the teams in the AL East, the Blue Jays have won the division the most times.

    a. True
    b. False

QUIZ ANSWERS

1. D – They have always been the Blue Jays
2. B - 1977
3. True
4. B – American League East
5. A – True
6. C - 2
7. A - Ace
8. B – Cito Gaston
9. D – Buffalo Bisons
10. B – Roy Hartsfield
11. True
12. C – TD Ballpark
13. C - 7
14. A - 2
15. True
16. D – Exhibition Stadium
17. B – 1 (2016)
18. B - 6
19. D – Atlanta Braves (National League East)
20. B – False (Yankees)

DID YOU KNOW?

1. The Blue Jays' franchise has had 16 different managers. They are Roy Hartsfield, Harry Warner, Bobby Mattick, Bobby Cox, Jimy Williams, Cito Gaston, Gene Tenace, Mel Queen, Tim Johnson, Jim Fregosi, Buck Martinez, Cookie Rojas, Carlos Tosca, John Gibbons, John Farrell, and Charlie Montoyo.

2. The Blue Jays were approved as a part of the 1977 MLB expansion, added alongside the Seattle Mariners.

3. Cito Gaston is the Toronto Blue Jays' all-time winningest manager with a record of 894-837 (.516) W-L%.

4. Roberto Alomar was the first player to be inducted into the National Baseball Hall of Fame as a Blue Jay. He was also the first player to have his jersey number retired by the Blue Jays.

5. The Toronto Blue Jays have hosted one MLB All-Star Game so far. It took place in 1991 at the SkyDome (Rogers Centre).

6. Only one Blue Jay has ever thrown a no-hitter in franchise history. It was thrown by Dave Stieb on September 2, 1991, against the Cleveland Indians.

7. No Blue Jays pitcher has ever thrown a perfect game.

8. The Blue Jays' AA team is the New Hampshire Fisher Cats.

9. During the 7th-inning stretch, before singing the classic, "Take Me Out to the Ballgame", fans sing along to "OK Blue Jays" by Keith Hampshire and the Bat Boys. It was released back in 1983.

10. The Blue Jays were originally owned by the Labatt Brewing Company, makers of Labatt's Blue beer.

CHAPTER 2:

JERSEYS & NUMBERS

QUIZ TIME!

1. The Blue Jays wore special red and white uniforms during the 2017 season to celebrate the 150th anniversary of Canada.

    a. True
    b. False

2. Which number is not retired by the Toronto Blue Jays (as of 2019 season)?

    a. 12
    b. 27
    c. 32
    d. 42

3. In the year 2000, the Blue Jays debuted a vest-style jersey.

    a. True
    b. False

4. What uniform number does Vladimir Guerrero Jr. wear for the Blue Jays?

   a. 23
   b. 25
   c. 27
   d. 29

5. What uniform number did first baseman Carlos Delgado NOT wear during his time as a member of the Blue Jays?

   a. 6
   b. 21
   c. 25
   d. 34

6. What uniform number did pitcher Dave Stieb wear during his time with the Blue Jays?

   a. 17
   b. 27
   c. 37
   d. 47

7. No Blue Jays player has ever worn the uniform No. 0.

   a. True
   b. False

8. Who is the only Blue Jays player to ever wear No. 99?

   a. Hyun-jin Ryu
   b. Rene Gonzales
   c. John Axford
   d. Ryan Dull

9. Which former Blue Jays legend has his No. 32 retired by the team?

    a. Roberto Alomar
    b. Roy Halladay
    c. Carlos Delgado
    d. José Bautista

10. The Blue Jays debuted powder blue uniforms in the 1980s with waistband pants sans-belts and a pullover jersey.

    a. True
    b. False

11. What are the Toronto Blue Jays' official team colors?

    a. Royal blue, navy blue, blood red, wedding dress white
    b. Navy blue, scarlet red, picket fence white
    c. Powder blue, baby blue, red, white
    d. Royal blue, navy blue, red, white

12. Who was the first Blue Jay to have his uniform number retired by the team?

    a. Roy Halladay
    b. Roberto Alomar
    c. Carlos Delgado
    d. Dave Stieb

13. The Blue Jays have retired only two numbers besides Jackie Robinson's No. 42. They have retired Roberto Alomar's No. 12 and Roy Halladay's No. 32.

    a. True
    b. False

14. What jersey number did Tony Fernández wear as a Blue Jay?

    a. 1
    b. 2
    c. 3
    d. 4

15. What jersey number did Jesse Barfield wear as a Blue Jay?

    a. 26
    b. 27
    c. 28
    d. 29

16. What jersey number did George Bell wear as a Blue Jay?

    a. 9
    b. 10
    c. 11
    d. 21

17. What jersey number did Roger Clemens wear as a Blue Jay?

    a. 12
    b. 21
    c. 22
    d. 45

18. What jersey number did Alfredo Griffin wear as a Blue Jay?

    a. 3
    b. 4

c. 8

d. 16

19. What jersey number did John Olerud wear as a Blue Jay?

    a. 5

    b. 9

    c. 18

    d. 19

20. What jersey number did Edwin Encarnacion NOT wear during his time as a member of the Blue Jays?

    a. 3

    b. 7

    c. 10

    d. 12

QUIZ ANSWERS

1. A - True

2. B – 27

3. A - True

4. C – 27

5. D – 34

6. C – 37

7. False, Al Oliver (1985)

8. A – Hyun-jin Ryu (2020)

9. B – Roy Halladay

10. True

11. D – Royal blue, navy blue, red, white

12. B – Roberto Alomar

13. True

14. A – 1

15. D – 29

16. C – 11

17. B - 21

18. B – 4

19. B – 9

20. A – 3

DID YOU KNOW?

1. Cliff Johnson is the only Blue Jays player to ever wear uniform No. 00. He wore it from 1985 to 1986.

2. Peter Munro is the only Blue Jays player to wear No. 69, Beau Taylor is the only Blue Jay to wear No. 72, Ryan Dull is the only Blue Jay to wear No. 73, Breyvic Valera is the only Blue Jay to wear No. 74, John Axford is the only Blue Jay to wear No. 77, Rene Gonzales is the only Blue Jay to wear No. 88, and Hyun Jin Ryu is the only Blue Jay to wear No. 99. (So far.)

3. The Blue Jays retired Roberto Alomar's No. 12 in 2011. They decided to retire Roy Halladay's No. 32 following his tragic death in November of 2017. They are currently the only two players to have their numbers retired by the team.

4. You may think the Blue Jays don't have a lot of retired numbers, but they actually DON'T have the least number of retirees. The Miami Marlins have retired ZERO player numbers.

5. José Bautista wore both No. 23 and No. 19 over his 10 years in Toronto.

6. Pitcher Jimmy Key wore both No. 27 and No. 22 over his 9 years in Toronto.

7. The Blue Jays' mascot, Ace, wears uniform No. 00.

8. Centerfielder Lloyd Moseby wore No. 15 as a member of the Blue Jays.

9. Current Blue Jay Vladimir Guerrero Jr. wears No. 27, just like his dad wore during his time in the MLB. Vlad Guerrero Sr. wore No. 27 for every team he played for over his 16-season career; the Montreal Expos, the Los Angeles Angels of Anaheim, the Texas Rangers, and the Baltimore Orioles.

10. Pitcher Jim Clancy wore No. 18 during all 12 of his years spent in Toronto.

CHAPTER 3:

FAMOUS QUOTES

QUIZ TIME!

1. Which famous Blue Jay once said: "I always believed no matter where you are, as long as you're doing what you love doing, you're going to be happy"?

   a. José Bautista
   b. Dave Stieb
   c. Roy Halladay
   d. Roberto Alomar

2. Which former Blue Jays pitcher once said: "Everybody kind of perceives me as being angry. It's not anger, it's motivation"?

   a. Dave Stieb
   b. Roger Clemens
   c. Roy Halladay
   d. Jimmy Key

3. Which former Blue Jay is quoted as saying: "Complaining is like vomiting. You might feel better after you get it out, but you make everybody around you sick"?

a. John Olerud

b. Dave Winfield

c. Paul Molitor

d. Shannon Stewart

4. Which former Blue Jay once said: "If my uniform isn't dirty, I haven't done anything in the baseball game"?

   a. Jose Canseco

   b. Rickey Henderson

   c. Edwin Encarnacion

   d. George Bell

5. Which former Blue Jay is quoted as saying: "I've always tried to work hard. I'm not trying to show anybody up or do something spectacular for attention"?

   a. Lloyd Moseby

   b. Josh Donaldson

   c. Roy Halladay

   d. Buck Martinez

6. Which former Blue Jay is quoted as saying, when asked about the MLB playoffs: "When you have 50,000 fans screaming, it kind of numbs the pain a little bit. It gives you that extra little jolt of adrenaline"?

   a. Josh Donaldson

   b. Justin Smoak

   c. José Bautista

   d. J.A. Happ

7. Which former Blue Jay is quoted as saying: "A lot of people have the ability, but they don't put forth the effort"?

    a. Tony Fernández
    b. David Wells
    c. Troy Tulowitzki
    d. Joe Carter

8. Former Blue Jays second baseman, Roberto Alomar once said, "A life is not important except in the impact it has on other lives."

    a. True
    b. False

9. Which former Blue Jays pitcher is quoted as saying: "The more I grew as a human being, the better I became at my craft"?

    a. Roy Halladay
    b. Dave Stieb
    c. R.A. Dickey
    d. A.J. Burnett

10. Which former Blue Jay is quoted as saying: "I'm very proud to be Canadian, not only to represent the Blue Jays, but my country"?

    a. Michael Saunders
    b. Brett Lawrie
    c. Russell Martin
    d. Lloyd Moseby

11. Which former Blue Jays pitcher is quoted as saying: "I have always been a passionate player and person. I often wear my emotions on my sleeve, sometimes for better, sometimes for worse. I hope that my teammates always respect that of me, as I trust they know my commitment to winning"?

    a. A.J. Burnett
    b. Dave Stieb
    c. Pat Hentgen
    d. Duane Ward

12. Which former Blue Jays manager is quoted as saying: "If you don't change direction, you end up where you are headed"?

    a. Cito Gaston
    b. John Gibbons
    c. Jimy Williams
    d. Bobby Cox

13. Which former Blue Jays pitcher is quoted as saying: "Never say never in this game because crazy stuff can happen"?

    a. Roy Halladay
    b. Brett Cecil
    c. Chris Carpenter
    d. Mark Buehrle

14. Which Blue Jay is quoted as saying: "Everything I learned about the game of baseball, I learned from my dad"?

a. Vladimir Guerrero Jr.

b. Roberto Alomar

c. Cavan Biggio

d. Bo Bichette

15. Which former Blue Jays player is quoted on his impending free agency as saying: "Hometown discounts don't exist, not in my world. In my eyes, I've given this organization a five-year hometown discount"?

a. Dave Stieb

b. José Bautista

c. Jose Canseco

d. Shawn Greene

16. Blue Jays shortstop Tony Fernández once said, "Never allow the fear of striking out keep you from playing the game."

a. True

b. False

17. Paul Molitor is quoted as saying, "Your mind has a way of putting limitations on your goals. When you persevere, you develop _____. Nobody knows their ceiling."

a. Character

b. Passion

c. Drive

d. Responsibility

18. Which former Blue Jays pitcher once said: "I think anything is possible if you have the mindset and the will and the desire to do it and put the time in"?

a. Roy Halladay

b. Dave Stieb

c. David Wells

d. Roger Clemens

19. Which former Blue Jays catcher once said: "My dad and mom had to sacrifice so much and had to teach us and show us the way of going about things, how to be humble, all those things. They helped us stay on track for what we wanted to do"?

a. Dioner Navarro

b. Bengie Molina

c. Pat Borders

d. Gregg Zaun

20. Former Blue Jay Scott Rolen once said: "I enjoy coming to the ballpark every day. I don't go to work. I come here to play."

a. True

b. False

QUIZ ANSWERS

1. D – Roberto Alomar

2. B – Roger Clemens

3. C – Paul Molitor

4. B – Rickey Henderson

5. C – Roy Halladay

6. A – Josh Donaldson

7. D – Joe Carter

8. B – False (Jackie Robinson)

9. C – R.A. Dickey

10. A – Michael Saunders

11. A – A.J. Burnett

12. B – John Gibbons

13. D – Mark Buehrle

14. B – Roberto Alomar

15. B – José Bautista

16. B – False (Babe Ruth)

17. A – Character

18. C – Albert Pujols

19. B – Bengie Molina

20. True

DID YOU KNOW?

1. "The 1989 team was one of the most fun teams that I ever managed. I took over from Jimy and we came back to win the division. That was a team that could manufacture runs anytime we wanted to." – Cito Gaston

2. "A ballplayer doesn't make excuses." – Roberto Alomar

3. "On some nights, you could totally predict that he was going to do something special." – A.J. Burnett on Roy Halladay

4. "I've always tried to do my best on the ball field. I can't do any more than that. I always give one hundred percent; and if my team loses, I come back and give one hundred perfect the next day." – Jesse Barfield

5. "I chose baseball because, to me, baseball is the best game of all." – Dave Winfield

6. "Go chase your dreams. Go get it. Don't let anyone tell you anything different. When people doubt you, use it as fire. Don't let it push you the wrong way. Don't let it take away from you working harder. Don't let it discourage you. Just use it. Let it build in the back of your head and deep in your chest, and when you get there to perform, just let it consume you and eat you up. That's when you let it all come out." – Marcus Stroman

7. "He is one of the most talented guys I ever played with and against. He was great at the plate and in the field and

made plays at second base that I never saw anyone else make." – Cal Ripken Jr. on Roberto Alomar

8. My heart is half Puerto Rican, half Canadian. That is how I feel." – Roberto Alomar

9. "When I was a kid, I used to play marbles. I know some of you think I've lost mine." – Jimy Williams

10. "To both of the teams that we were blessed to be a part of — the Blue Jays and the Phillies. Thank you for allowing us to grow up, to fail over and over and finally learn how to succeed within your organizations. There were some really amazing years but there were some really tough ones, too, and you never gave up on him.

11. "More than anything, he would want both organizations to know that they hold a huge place in our heart and always will. Evidence of their love for us and our love for them, as well, was shown all week as they came together as one to celebrate Roy — and that means the world to me. To both organizations, I can't thank you enough.

12. "I think that Roy would want everyone to know that people are not perfect. We are all imperfect and flawed in one way or another. We all struggle, but with hard work, humility, and dedication, imperfect people can still have perfect moments. Roy was blessed in his life and in his career to have some perfect moments, but I believe that they were only possible because of the man he strived to be, the teammate that he was, and the people that he was so blessed to be on the field with." – Brandy Halladay's

Speech at the late Roy Halladay's National Baseball Hall of Fame Induction Ceremony

CHAPTER 4:

CATCHY NICKNAMES

QUIZ TIME!

1. Which nickname does Roberto Alomar go by?

   a. Rob

   b. Robbie

   c. Ally

   d. Ro-Al

2. José Bautista goes by the nickname "Joey Bats."

   a. True

   b. False

3. What was Roy Halladay's real first name?

   a. John

   b. Ryan

   c. Michael

   d. Harry

4. What was Roy Halladay's famous nickname?

   a. Hally

   b. Doc

c. Roy-Hall

d. Uncle

5. Which is NOT a nickname for the Blue Jays as a team?

a. The Jays

b. The Blue Birds

c. The Birds in Blue

d. The BJ's

6. What was pitcher Dave Stieb's nickname?

a. Davey-S

b. Stieby

c. Uncle Dave

d. Sir David

7. "Roger" is Roger Clemens' middle name. "William" is his given first name.

a. True

b. False

8. Which nickname did former Blue Jays pitcher Roger Clemens go by?

a. Rocket

b. Clemmy

c. R- Clem

d. Willy

9. What nickname did former Blue Jay, Lloyd Moseby go by?

a. Mose

b. L.L. Moseby

c. Shaker

d. Mr. Moseby

10. What is the nickname of former Blue Jays third baseman Josh Donaldson?

   a. Donnie

   b. The Bringer of Rain

   c. Joshy D

   d. JD Slugger

11. What was former Blue Jay Fred McGriff's nickname?

   a. Sluggin' Fred

   b. Freddie

   c. Griffey

   d. Crime Dog

12. Roy Halladay got the nickname "Doc" because he was a pediatrician during the baseball offseason.

   a. True

   b. False

13. Former Blue Jay Tony Fernández's nickname was "El Cabeza." What is "el cabeza" Spanish for?

   a. The Fastest

   b. The Head

   c. The Legs

   d. The Strong

14. What was former Blue Jay, John Olerud's nickname?

   a. Ole

   b. Big Rude

c. Johnny O

d. Both B and C

15. During MLB Players' Weekend in 2018, catcher Russell Martin wore the nickname "El Muscle" on the back of his uniform. He is often called "Russell Le Muscle."

a. True

b. False

16. Former Blue Jay Troy Tulowitzki goes by the nickname _____.

a. TT

b. Tulo

c. That Boy Troy

d. Both A and B

17. Dave Winfield was nicknamed "Daddy Longlegs" after his long legs, size, and his domination out in right field.

a. True

b. False

18. What nickname did first baseman Justin Smoak go by during 2018's MLB Players' Weekend?

a. Smoaky Bear

b. Smoakin'

c. Just-in Time

d. Moakey

19. During 2018's MLB Players' Weekend, what nickname did Blue Jays pitcher Ken Giles go by?

a. Kenny G
b. A Gile a Minute
c. 100 Miles Giles
d. Ken't Stop

20. Former Blue Jays outfielder Curtis Granderson goes by the hilarious nickname, "The Grandyman."

a. True
b. False

QUIZ ANSWERS

1. B – Robbie
2. True
3. D – Harry
4. B - Doc
5. C – The Birds in Blue
6. D – Sir David
7. True
8. A – Rocket
9. C – Shaker
10. B – The Bringer of Rain
11. D – Crime Dog
12. B – False
13. B – The Head
14. D – Both B and C
15. A - True
16. B – Tulo
17. A – True
18. D – Moakey
19. C – 100 Miles Giles
20. A – True

DID YOU KNOW?

1. Cavan Biggio is the son of MLB Hall-of-Famer Craig Biggio. He goes by the nickname, "Biggy."

2. Teoscar Hernandez is known for giving his teammates a "seed shower" after they hit a home run. During 2019's MLB Players' Weekend, he went by the nickname, "Mr. Seeds."

3. Lourdes Gurriel Jr. is known for his hairstyle, which resembles a pineapple. "Piña" means "pineapple" in Spanish. So, on MLB's Players' Weekend in 2019, he went by the nickname "#PIÑAPOWER JR." …. Can't forget that hashtag.

4. For MLB Players' Weekend in 2019, Reese McGuire went by the nickname "Pieces"…. Get it? Reese's Pieces!

5. Former Blue Jays pitcher R.A. Dickey's real name is Robert Allen Dickey.

6. Former Blue Jay Devon White went by the nickname "Devo."

7. Chris Berman gave former Blue Jay Alfredo Griffin the nickname "Fettuccine Alfredo."

8. Former Blue Jays pitcher Al Leiter's full first name is Alois Leiter.

9. Paul Molitor went by the nicknames "Molly" and "The Ignitor."

10. "Cito" is a nickname. Cito Gaston's real name is Clarence.

CHAPTER 5:

DOC

QUIZ TIME!

1. What was Roy Halladay's full name?

    a. Leroy Harry Halladay III
    b. Harry Leroy Halladay III
    c. Leroy Ryan Halladay III
    d. Ryan Leroy Halladay III

2. Roy Halladay played his entire 16-season MLB career with the Toronto Blue Jays.

    a. True
    b. False

3. Where was Roy Halladay born?

    a. Miami, Florida
    b. San Diego, California
    c. Dallas, Texas
    d. Denver, Colorado

4. When was Roy Halladay born?

    a. November 7, 1967
    b. May 14, 1967
    c. May 14, 1977
    d. November 7, 1977

5. Roy Halladay was elected to the National Baseball Hall of Fame posthumously in 2019 with 85.4% of the vote.

    a. True
    b. False

6. How many games did Roy Halladay win for the Blue Jays in 2003?

    a. 19
    b. 22
    c. 24
    d. 11

7. How many MLB All-Star Games was Roy Halladay named to during his career?

    a. 2
    b. 4
    c. 13
    d. 8

8. As a member of the Philadelphia Phillies, Roy Halladay threw the second postseason no-hitter in MLB history against the Cincinnati Reds on October 6, 2010.

    a. True
    b. False

9. Roy Halladay was selected in the _____ round of the 1995 MLB draft by the Toronto Blue Jays.

    a. 1st
    b. 2nd
    c. 10th
    d. 201th

10. What uniform number did Roy Halladay NEVER wear during his career?

    a. 32
    b. 33
    c. 34
    d. 52

11. How old was Roy Halladay when he passed away in 2017 in a plane crash?

    a. 37
    b. 40
    c. 43
    d. 49

12. Roy Halladay is the only pitcher in MLB history to have more hits at the plate himself than he allowed in the postseason.

    a. True
    b. False

13. Who gave Roy Halladay's Hall of Fame speech for him posthumously in 2019?

    a. His son, Ryan
    b. His son, Braden

c. His wife, Brandy

d. His dad, Harry Halladay Jr.

14. In 2010, Roy Halladay became only the fifth pitcher in MLB history to win a Cy Young Award in both the American and National leagues.

    a. True

    b. False

15. How many career saves did Roy Halladay collect?

    a. 0

    b. 1

    c. 6

    d. 18

16. How many career wins did Roy Halladay finish with?

    a. 199

    b. 200

    c. 203

    d. 213

17. Roy Halladay never got to pitch in the postseason with the Blue Jays.

    a. True

    b. False

18. What is Roy Halladay's career ERA?

    a. 2.59

    b. 3.59

    c. 2.38

    d. 3.38

19. Where did Roy Halladay attend high school?

    a. Pomona High School

    b. Arvada West High School

    c. Horizon High School

    d. Mountain Range High School

20. Roy Halladay finished his career with 2,117 strikeouts.

    a. True

    b. False

QUIZ ANSWERS

1. B – Harry Leroy Halladay III
2. B – False [Toronto Blue Jays (1998-2009), Philadelphia Phillies (2010-2013)]
3. D – Denver, Colorado
4. C – May 14, 1977
5. A – True
6. B – 22
7. D – 8
8. A – True
9. A – 1st
10. B – 33
11. B – 40
12. A – True
13. C – His wife, Brandy
14. A – True
15. B – 1
16. C – 203
17. A – True
18. D – 3.38
19. B – Arvada West High School
20. A – True

DID YOU KNOW?

1. On May 29, 2010, as a member of the Phillies, Roy Halladay threw a perfect game against the Marlins. Dallas Braden of the Oakland A's threw a perfect game just 20 days earlier. This was the first time two pitchers threw perfect games in the same month and the first time that more than one perfect game was thrown in the same season.

2. By the end of his career, the only team that Roy Halladay had never defeated was the Philadelphia Phillies. The only other team he never defeated in the regular season was the San Francisco Giants, but he did defeat them in the 2010 postseason during the NLCS.

3. Roy Halladay started the MLB All-Star Game for both the American and National Leagues.

4. Roy Halladay was on the cover of the video game MLB 2K11.

5. No batter struck out more times against Doc than Yankees legend, SS Derek Jeter.

6. While on a fishing trip, Roy Halladay once saved the life of a man who was being attacked by an anaconda.

7. Roy's nickname, "Doc," was given to him by Blue Jays announcer, Tom Cheek. His nickname was a reference to the Wild West's Doc Holliday.

8. "Toronto will forever hold a special place in my heart. The memories will last a lifetime and so will my gratitude." — Roy Halladay's closing statement in his farewell letter to Blue Jays fans in December 2009.

9. On March 29, 2018, during Opening Day ceremonies, the Toronto Blue Jays retired Doc's number 32 in the presence of his wife Brandy and their two sons, Ryan and Braden.

10. On November 7, 2017, Halladay took his ICON A5 Founders Edition amphibious plane up into the air near his Clearwater, Florida, home. He crashed to his death in the Gulf of Mexico, 10 miles west of St. Petersburg.

11. An autopsy showed that he may have been impaired at the time of the crash. According to the autopsy report released by the Pinellas-Pasco Medical Examiner's Office, Halladay had high concentrations of morphine and amphetamines in his system. Also present in his blood were an antidepressant, the sleeping aid Ambien, and trace amounts of alcohol.

12. Forensic pathologist Burr Hartman said that "He was impaired by these drugs. It was definitely not safe for him to fly an airplane. It's a cocktail that could have led to cardiac arrest, but it would have also impaired his coordination." – Society for American Baseball Research.

CHAPTER 6:

STATISTICALLY SPEAKING

QUIZ TIME!

1. Carlos Delgado holds the franchise record for home runs. How many did he hit?

    a. 400
    b. 336
    c. 288
    d. 397

2. Pitcher Dave Stieb has the most wins in Toronto Blue Jays franchise history with 175.

    a. True
    b. False

3. How many appearances have the Blue Jays made in the playoffs?

    a. 2
    b. 3
    c. 7
    d. 10

4. Which former Blue Jays batter holds the single-season record for strikeouts, with 170 in 2017?

   a. Justin Smoak
   b. Colby Rasmus
   c. Michael Saunders
   d. José Bautista

5. Which pitcher has the most strikeouts in Blue Jays franchise history with a whopping 1,658?

   a. Roy Halladay
   b. Dave Stieb
   c. Jim Clancy
   d. David Wells

6. Who has the most stolen bases in Blue Jays franchise history with 255?

   a. Roberto Alomar
   b. Shannon Stewart
   c. Rajai Davis
   d. Lloyd Moseby

7. Billy Koch holds the record for most saves in Blue Jays history, with 217.

   a. True
   b. False

8. Who is the Blue Jays' all-time winningest manager?

   a. Charles Comiskey
   b. Mike Matheny
   c. Branch Rickey
   d. Tony LaRussa

9. Which player holds the Blue Jays franchise record for home runs in a single season with 54?

   a. José Bautista
   b. Jose Canseco
   c. Josh Donaldson
   d. George Bell

10. Who holds the single-season Blue Jays record for hits with 215?

   a. Tony Fernández
   b. Paul Molitor
   c. Vernon Wells
   d. Carlos Delgado

11. Who holds the single-season Blue Jays record for double plays grounded into with 25?

   a. Lyle Overbay
   b. Edwin Encarnacion
   c. Ed Sprague
   d. Troy Glaus

12. Joe Carter holds the record for the most sacrifice flies in Blue Jays history with 65.

   a. True
   b. False

13. Who threw the most wild pitches in Blue Jays franchise history with 88?

   a. Jim Clancy
   b. Juan Guzman

c. Roy Halladay

d. Pat Hentgen

14. Tony Fernández holds the Blue Jays single-season record for most triples. How many did he hit in his record 1990 season?

    a. 13

    b. 15

    c. 17

    d. 22

15. Which hitter drew the most walks in Blue Jays franchise history with 827?

    a. José Bautista

    b. Willie Upshaw

    c. Carlos Delgado

    d. John Olerud

16. Which Blue Jays hitter holds the all-time franchise record for best overall batting average at .315?

    a. Roberto Alomar

    b. Paul Molitor

    c. Frank Catalaotto

    d. Dámaso García

17. Carlos Delgado has the most doubles and RBIs in Blue Jays franchise history.

    a. True

    b. False

18. Carlos Delgado has the most plate appearances all-time in Cardinals franchise history with how many?

    a. 5,799
    b. 5,900
    c. 5,963
    d. 6,018

19. Which pitcher holds the franchise record for most saves in a single season with 45?

    a. Duane Ward
    b. Roberto Osuna
    c. Tom Henke
    d. Kevin Gregg

20. Jim Clancy holds the Blue Jays franchise record for most losses with 140.

    a. True
    b. False

QUIZ ANSWERS

1. B – 336

2. A – True

3. C – 7

4. D – José Bautista

5. B – Dave Stieb

6. D – Lloyd Moseby

7. B – False, Tom Henke

8. C – Cito Gaston (894-837 .516 W-L%)

9. A – José Bautista (2010)

10. C – Vernon Wells (2003)

11. D – Troy Glaus (2006)

12. A – True

13. B – Juan Guzman

14. C – 17

15. C – Carlos Delgado

16. B – Paul Molitor

17. True

18. D – 6,018

19. A – Duane Ward (1993)

20. A – True

DID YOU KNOW?

1. Dave Stieb threw the most innings in Blue Jays franchise history with 2,873. Coming in second is Jim Clancy who threw 2,204.2 innings.

2. John Olerud had the best single-season batting average in Blue Jays franchise history at .363 in 1993. Carlos Delgado is second with a batting average of .344 in 2000.

3. Devon White holds the Blue Jays franchise record for stolen base percentage with 84.56% success. Lloyd Moseby holds the franchise record for stolen bases with 255. Tony Fernández, Dámaso García, and Lloyd Moseby are all tired for the most times caught stealing with 86 each.

4. Carlos Delgado has the most extra-base hits in Blue Jays franchise history with 690. Second on the list is Vernon Wells with 592.

5. Carlos Delgado holds the Blue Jays franchise record for at-bats per home run with 14.9. Essentially what this means is that during his time with Toronto, Delgado hit a home run about every 15 at-bats.

6. Alfredo Griffin holds the Blue Jays single-season record for times caught stealing with 2 in 1980.

7. Shea Hillenbrand holds the single-season Blue Jays record for the most hit by pitches with 22 in 2005.

8. Vernon Wells has grounded into the most double plays in Blue Jays history with 146.

9. Roy Halladay holds the Blue Jays single-season record for wins with 22 in 2003. Second on the list is a tie between Roger Clemens with 21 in 1997 and Jack Morris with 21 in 1992.

10. Jerry Garvin and Phil Huffman are tied for the most losses pitched in a single season in Blue Jays history. Garvin had 18 losses in 977 and Huffman had 18 losses in 1979.

CHAPTER 7:

THE TRADE MARKET

QUIZ TIME!

1. On December 5, 1990, the Toronto Blue Jays traded 1B Fred McGriff and SS Tony Fernández to the San Diego Padres in exchange for who?

    a. Roberto Alomar and Rickey Henderson
    b. Roberto Alomar and Dave Winfield
    c. Joe Carter and David Wells
    d. Joe Carter and Roberto Alomar

2. On August 21, 2008, the Blue Jays traded C Robinzon Diaz to the Pittsburgh Pirates in exchange for whom?

    a. A.J. Burnett
    b. Rod Barajas
    c. José Bautista
    d. Lyle Overbay

3. The Toronto Blue Jays NEVER traded Roy Halladay.

    a. True
    b. False

4. On November 28, 2014, the Toronto Blue Jays traded INF Franklin Barreto, RHP Kendall Graveman, 3B Brett Lawrie, and LHP Sean Nolin to the Oakland A's in exchange for who?

    a. Rajai Davis
    b. Liam Hendricks
    c. Eric Sogard
    d. Josh Donaldson

5. On July 6, 1986, Toronto traded RHP Doyle Alexander to the Atlanta Braves in exchange for RHP Duane Ward.

    a. True
    b. False

6. What year did the Blue Jays acquire Rickey Henderson from the Oakland A's?

    a. 1992
    b. 1993
    c. 1995
    d. 1997

7. On July 30, 2015, the Toronto Blue Jays traded LHP's Daniel Norris, Jairo Labourt, and Matthew Boyd to the Detroit Tigers in exchange for whom?

    a. David Price
    b. Phil Coke
    c. Francisco Liriano
    d. Curtis Granderson

8. Which team traded RHP David Cone to the Blue Jays on August 27, 1992?

    a. Boston Red Sox

    b. Kansas City Royals

    c. New York Mets

    d. New York Yankees

9. On February 18, 1999, the Toronto Blue Jays traded which player to the New York Yankees in exchange for LHP's David Wells & Graeme Lloyd and IF Homer Bush?

    a. Roger Clemens

    b. Dave Winfield

    c. Cecil Fielder

    d. Jose Canseco

10. The Blue Jays traded Noah Syndergaard to the New York Mets in 2012.

    a. True

    b. False

11. On July 27, 2011, the Toronto Blue Jays acquired Colby Lewis, Trever Miller, Brian Tallet, and P.J. Walters from which team, in exchange for RHP Octavio Dotel, RHP Edwin Jackson, CF Corey Patterson, and LHP Marc Rzepczynski?

    a. Detroit Tigers

    b. New York Yankees

    c. St. Louis Cardinals

    d. Tampa Bay Rays

12. The Blue Jays have only made five trades with the Tampa Bay Rays (as of the end of the 2019 season) ever.

    a. True
    b. False

13. How many trades have the Blue Jays made with the Colorado Rockies all-time (as of the 2019 season)?

    a. 7
    b. 9
    c. 11
    d. 21

14. The Blue Jays have never made a trade with the Chicago Cubs.

    a. True
    b. False

15. On July 19, 2000, the Toronto Blue Jays traded Michael Young and Darwin Cubillán to which team, in exchange for Esteban Loaiza?

    a. Chicago White Sox
    b. Philadelphia Phillies
    c. Los Angeles Dodgers
    d. Texas Rangers

16. On July 31, 2009, the Toronto Blue Jays traded Scott Rolen to the Cincinnati Reds in exchange for Josh Roenicke, Zach Stewart, and which third player?

    a. Yunel Escobar
    b. Lyle Overbay

c. Edwin Encarnacion

d. Travis Snider

17. How many trades have the Toronto Blue Jays made with the St. Louis Cardinals all-time (as of the 2019 season)?

a. 1

b. 5

c. 10

d. 15

18. On January 21, 2011, who did the Toronto Blue Jays trade to the Los Angeles Angels of Anaheim in exchange for Mike Napoli and Juan Rivera?

a. Alex Rios

b. Marc Rzepczynski

c. Aaron Hill

d. Vernon Wells

19. The Blue Jays have made how many trades with the Oakland Athletics in franchise history (as of the end of the 2019 season)?

a. 47

b. 37

c. 27

d. 17

20. On September 22, 1987, the Blue Jays acquired Juan Guzman from the Los Angeles Dodgers in exchange for Mike Sharperson.

a. True

b. False

QUIZ ANSWERS

1. D – Joe Carter and Roberto Alomar
2. C – José Bautista
3. B – False, On December 16, 2009, the Blue Jays traded Halladay to the Philadelphia Phillies for Travis d'Arnaud, Kyle Drabek, and Michael Taylor
4. D – Josh Donaldson
5. A – True
6. B – 1993
7. A – David Price
8. C – New York Mets
9. A – Roger Clemens
10. A – True
11. C – St. Louis Cardinals
12. A – True
13. B – 9
14. B – False (8)
15. D – Texas Rangers
16. C – Edwin Encarnacion
17. C – 10
18. D – Vernon Wells
19. B – 37
20. A – True

DID YOU KNOW?

1. On November 19, 2012, the Toronto Blue Jays traded Henderson Álvarez III, Anthony DeSclafani, Yunel Escobar, Adeiny Hechavarria, Jake Marisnick, Jeff Mathis, and Justin Nicolino to the Miami Marlins in exchange for José Reyes, Emilio Bonifácio, John Buck, Mark Buehrle, Josh Johnson, and cash.

2. The Toronto Blue Jays have made only seven trades with the Boston Red Sox all-time (as of the end of the 2019 season).

3. On July 20, 2012, the Toronto Blue Jays traded Francisco Cordero, Joseph Musgrove, David Rollins, Carlos Perez, Ben Francisco, Asher Wojciechowski, and Kevin Comer to the Houston Astros in exchange for J.A. Happ, Brandon Lyon, and David Carpenter.

4. On October 30, 2014, the Toronto Blue Jays traded C Santiago Nessy to the Kansas City Royals for P Liam Hendricks.

5. On November 1, 2014, the Toronto Blue Jays traded 1B Adam Lind to the Milwaukee Brewers in exchange for P Marcos Estrada.

6. On December 5, 1978, the Toronto Blue Jays traded Victor Cruz to the Cleveland Indians in exchange for Alfredo Griffin and Phil Lansford (brother of Carney and Jody).

7. On January 11, 2019, the Toronto Blue Jays traded Russell Martin and cash to the Los Angeles Dodgers in exchange for Ronny Brito (minors) and Andrew Sopko (minors).

8. The Toronto Blue Jays have made only eight trades with the Minnesota Twins (as of the end of the 2019 season).

9. On August 31, 2018, the Toronto Blue Jays traded Curtis Granderson to the Milwaukee Brewers in exchange for Demi Orimoloye (minors).

10. The Toronto Blue Jays have made only six trades with the San Francisco Giants (as of the end of the 2019 season).

CHAPTER 8:

DRAFT DAY

QUIZ TIME!

1. Which MLB team selected José Bautista in the 20th round of the 2000 MLB draft?

   a. Toronto Blue Jays
   b. Baltimore Orioles
   c. Pittsburgh Pirates
   d. Kansas City Royals

2. With the 2nd overall pick in first round of the 1978 MLB draft, the Toronto Blue Jays selected which player?

   a. John Mayberry
   b. Alfredo Griffin
   c. Barry Bonnell
   d. Lloyd Moseby

3. The Toronto Blue Jays selected IF Cavan Biggio in the 5th round of the 2016 MLB draft from which college?

   a. Cal State Monterey Bay
   b. Seton Hall University

c. University of Notre Dame

d. Yale University

4. With which pick overall in the first round of the 1995 MLB draft did the Toronto Blue Jays select RHP Roy Halladay?

    a. 1st

    b. 7th

    c. 10th

    d. 17th

5. With the 22nd overall pick in first round of the 2012 MLB draft, the Toronto Blue Jays selected RHP Marcus Stroman from which school?

    a. San Diego State University

    b. Stanford University

    c. Duke University

    d. UC Davis

6. With the 15th overall pick in the first round of the 1993 MLB draft, the Toronto Blue Jays selected which right-handed pitcher?

    a. Chris Carpenter

    b. Pat Hentgen

    c. Juan Guzman

    d. Dave Stieb

7. Blue Jays shortstop Bo Bichette was drafted by the Blue Jays in the 2nd round of the 2016 MLB draft.

    a. True

    b. False

8. Left-handed pitcher Al Leiter was drafted in the 2nd round of the 1984 MLB draft by which team?

    a. New York Yankees

    b. New York Mets

    c. Florida Marlins

    d. Toronto Blue Jays

9. Dave Stieb was drafted by the Toronto Blue Jays in which round of the 1978 MLB draft?

    a. 1st

    b. 3rd

    c. 5th

    d. 8th

10. Josh Donaldson was drafted in the 1st round, 48th overall, in the 2007 MLB draft by the Oakland Athletics.

    a. True

    b. False

11. In the first round of the 1996 MLB draft, the Toronto Blue Jays selected right-handed pitcher Billy Koch as what pick overall?

    a. 1st

    b. 4th

    c. 7th

    d. 11th

12. Stephen Strasburg was chosen first overall in the first round of the 2009 MLB draft by the Toronto Blue Jays.

    a. True

    b. False

13. Shannon Stewart was drafted in which round of the 1992 MLB draft by the Toronto Blue Jays?

    a. 1st

    b. 3rd

    c. 20th

    d. 13th

14. The Toronto Blue Jays selected catcher Pat Borders in the 6th round of what MLB draft?

    a. 1986

    b. 1984

    c. 1982

    d. 1980

15. Right-handed pitcher A.J. Burnett was drafted by which team in the 8th round of the 1995 MLB draft?

    a. Florida Marlins

    b. New York Yankees

    c. Pittsburgh Pirates

    d. New York Mets

16. Left-handed pitcher Brett Cecil was drafted 38th overall in the first round of the 2007 MLB draft by which team?

    a. Toronto Blue Jays

    b. St. Louis Cardinals

    c. San Francisco Giants

    d. San Diego Padres

17. Which player did the Toronto Blue Jays select with the 19th overall pick in the first round of the 1999 MLB draft?

a. Josh Phelps

b. Eric Hinske

c. Alex Rios

d. Vernon Wells

18. With the 5th overall pick in the first round of the 1997 MLB draft, the Toronto Blue Jays selected which player?

a. Felipe Lopez

b. Vernon Wells

c. Kevin Witt

d. Gabe Gross

19. First baseman Justin Smoak was drafted by, but did not sign with, which team in 2005? He was then drafted again in 2008 by, and signed with, which team?

a. Oakland A's, Seattle Mariners

b. Texas Rangers, Seattle Mariners

c. Texas Rangers, Milwaukee Brewers

d. Oakland A's, Texas Rangers

20. Left-handed pitcher Mark Rzepczynski was drafted by the Toronto Blue Jays in the 5th round of the 2007 MLB draft.

a. True

b. False

QUIZ ANSWERS

1. C –Pittsburgh Pirates

2. D – Lloyd Moseby

3. C – University of Notre Dame

4. D – 17th

5. C – Duke University

6. A – Chris Carpenter

7. A – True

8. A – New York Yankees

9. C – 5th

10. B – False, Chicago Cubs

11. B – 4th

12. B – False, Washington Nationals

13. A – 1st

14. C – 1982

15. D – New York Mets

16. A – Toronto Blue Jays

17. A – Trevor Rosenthal

18. B – Vernon Wells

19. D – Oakland A's, Texas Rangers

20. A – True

DID YOU KNOW?

1. The St. Louis Cardinals selected former Blue Jays OF Colby Rasmus 28th overall in the first round of the 2005 MLB draft.

2. The Toronto Blue Jays selected 1B Joe Olerud in the 3rd round of the 1989 MLB draft.

3. The California Angels drafted former Blue Jay Devon White in the 6th round of the 1981 MLB draft.

4. The Chicago Cubs drafted former Blue Jay Joe Carter in the first round, 2nd overall in the 1981 MLB draft.

5. The Milwaukee Brewers drafted former Blue Jay Paul Molitor in the first round, 3rd overall in the 1977 MLB draft.

6. The Boston Red Sox drafted former Blue Jays RHP Roger Clemens in the first round, 19th overall in the 1983 MLB draft.

7. The Toronto Blue Jays drafted Jesse Barfield in the 9th round of the 1977 MLB draft.

8. The Toronto Blue Jays drafted LHP Jimmy Key in the 3rd round of the 1982 MLB draft.

9. The Toronto Blue Jays drafted RHP Pat Hentgen in the 5th round of the 1986 MLB draft.

10. The Texas Rangers drafted former Blue Jays RHP Jim Clancy in the 4th round of the 1974 MLB draft.

CHAPTER 9:

ODDS & ENDS

QUIZ TIME!

1. Which TV superhero actor is a huge Blue Jays fan in real life?

   a. Grant Gustin (The Flash)

   b. Stephen Amell (Green Arrow)

   c. Melissa Benoist (Supergirl)

   d. Cress Williams (Black Lightning)

2. Blue Jays pitcher Dave Stieb was once kissed on the mound by a fan who ran onto the field during a game.

   a. True

   b. False

3. Paul Molitor was the manager of which MLB team from 2015-2018?

   a. Toronto Blue Jays

   b. Milwaukee Brewers

   c. Chicago Cubs

   d. Minnesota Twins

4. Josh Donaldson found out that he had been traded to the Blue Jays while watching what?

    a. The Simpsons
    b. The Golf Channel
    c. Vikings
    d. Sportscenter

5. When Jose Canseco played for the Oakland A's, he and which teammate were considered the "Bash Brothers"?

    a. Rickey Henderson
    b. Dave Henderson
    c. Mark McGwire
    d. Carney Lansford

6. What is the name of the 2011 baseball documentary starring R.A. Dickey?

    a. Four Days in October
    b. Screwball
    c. Knuckleball
    d. No-No

7. When Cito Gaston played for the Atlanta Braves, he was Hank Aaron's roommates.

    a. True
    b. False

8. In 2008, Joe Carter appeared on an episode of which show?

    a. Trading Spaces
    b. Pros vs. Joes
    c. The Real Housewives of Orange County
    d. Survivor

9. What coaching position did Lloyd Moseby hold for the Blue Jays in 1998 and 1999?

   a. First
   b. Third
   c. Bench
   d. Hitting

10. Upon retiring from the MLB, Troy Tulowitzki was hired as a coach by which team?

   a. Long Beach State
   b. Colorado Rockies
   c. Texas Longhorns
   d. Toronto Blue Jays

11. David Wells has a tattoo of which famous MLB player?

   a. Joe DiMaggio
   b. Hank Aaron
   c. Jackie Robinson
   d. Babe Ruth

12. John Olerud is a cousin of former MLB player and manager Dale Sveum.

   a. True
   b. False

13. J.P. Arencibia was once married to a member of which band?

   a. Paramore
   b. Little Big Town
   c. The Band Perry
   d. Little Mix

14. Which former Blue Jay is now an analyst for MLB Network?

    a. Mark DeRosa
    b. Mark McGwire
    c. Ozzie Smith
    d. Lance Berkman

15. Frank Thomas owns his own beer brand, named what?

    a. Thomas Beer & Co.
    b. Big Hurt Brew
    c. Frank Brew
    d. Big Hurt Beer

16. Marcus Stroman is one of only six players shorter than 5 feet 10 inches to make a start in the MLB in the 21st century.

    a. True
    b. False

17. Which former Blue Jay has a daughter who played two seasons in the WNBA?

    a. Devon White
    b. Lloyd Moseby
    c. Roberto Alomar
    d. George Bell

18. Cookie Rojas' son, Victor is a play-by-play announcer for which MLB team?

    a. Los Angeles Angels of Anaheim
    b. Philadelphia Phillies

c. Boston Red Sox

d. Minnesota Twins

19. Who has played for more MLB teams than any other player in MLB history?

    a. Rickey Henderson

    b. Omar Vizquel

    c. Rajai Davis

    d. Edwin Jackson

20. A species of weevil, *Sicoderus bautistai,* was named after José Bautista in 2018.

    a. True

    b. False

QUIZ ANSWERS

1. B – Stephen Amell (Green Arrow)

2. A – True

3. D – Minnesota Twins

4. B – The Golf Channel

5. C – Mark McGwire

6. C – Knuckleball

7. A – True

8. B – Pros vs. Joes

9. A – First

10. C – Texas Longhorns

11. D – Babe Ruth

12. A – True

13. C – The Band Perry

14. A – Mark DeRosa

15. D – Big Hurt Beer

16. A – True

17. A – Devon White

18. A – Los Angeles Angels of Anaheim

19. D – Edwin Jackson

20. A – True

DID YOU KNOW?

1. Vernon Wells' father, Vernon Wells Jr., is an acclaimed sports artist and was an early contributor to Upper Deck baseball cards.

2. Cavan Biggio and Vladimir Guerrero Jr. were the first teammates in MLB history whose fathers are both Hall-of-Famers.

3. Bo Bichette is named after Bo Jackson. Bichette is the son of Dante Bichette, a former player who is now a coach with the Blue Jays.

4. Kevin Pillar named his daughter "Kobie" after Lakers and NBA legend, the late Kobe Bryant.

5. Joe Carter's walk-off home run celebration was used as track artwork for Drake's song, "Back to Back."

6. In the film *Big Daddy*, Jon Stewart's character said he fathered a child in Toronto as a by-product of celebrating Joe Carter's walk-off home run to win the 1993 World Series.

7. Both of Jesse Barfield's sons, Jeremy and Josh, played in the MLB as well. Jeremy played for the Oakland A's and Boston Red Sox organizations and Josh played for the San Diego Padres and Cleveland Indians.

8. Roy Halladay was the first player to be inducted into the National Baseball Hall of Fame posthumously by the BBWAA since Roberto Clemente in 1973.

9. Former Blue Jay Kevin Millar co-hosts MLB Network's *Intentional Talk* with Chris Rose. The show began back in April of 2011.

10. Former Blue Jay Dan Plesac has a nephew, Zach who currently pitches for the Cleveland Indians.

CHAPTER 10:

OUTFIELDERS

QUIZ TIME!

1. Dave Winfield played one season with the Toronto Blue Jays. Which of the teams below did he NOT play for during his 22-season career?

   a. Oakland Athletics
   b. New York Yankees
   c. San Diego Padres
   d. California Angels

2. Former Blue Jays left fielder George Bell was never named to an MLB All-Star Game in his 12-year MLB career.

   a. True
   b. False

3. How many Gold Glove Awards did former Blue Jays centerfielder Vernon Wells win over the course of his 15-year MLB career?

   a. 0
   b. 2

c. 3

d. 7

4. Rickey Henderson stole 22 bases in the 44 games he played for the Toronto Blue Jays.

    a. True

    b. False

5. Former Blue Jays centerfielder Lloyd Moseby played for two teams during his 12-year MLB career. He played for the Blue Jays and which other team?

    a. New York Mets

    b. San Diego Padres

    c. Pittsburgh Pirates

    d. Detroit Tigers

6. How many games did former Blue Jays outfielder Jose Canseco play in for the Jays during his lone season (1998) in Toronto?

    a. 133

    b. 151

    c. 154

    d. 162

7. Shannon Stewart played his entire 14-year MLB career with the Blue Jays franchise.

    a. True

    b. False

8. How many seasons did outfielder Rajai Davis play for the Blue Jays?

a. 2

b. 3

c. 4

d. 5

9. How many home runs did Joe Bautista hit for the Blue Jays during the 2010 season?

a. 39

b. 43

c. 54

d. 58

10. How many seasons did outfielder Joe Carter play for the Toronto Blue Jays?

a. 3

b. 5

c. 6

d. 7

11. Which team did former Blue Jays right fielder Shawn Green NOT play for during his 15-year MLB career?

a. Arizona Diamondbacks

b. Los Angeles Dodgers

c. Boston Red Sox

d. New York Mets

12. Right fielder Alex Rios hit 81 home runs over his six seasons with the Toronto Blue Jays.

a. True

b. False

13. How many hits did former Blue Jays outfielder Melky Cabrera collect during his two seasons in Toronto?

    a. 261
    b. 267
    c. 159
    d. 309

14. How many games did center fielder B.J. Upton play for the Toronto Blue Jays in 2016?

    a. 161
    b. 101
    c. 88
    d. 57

15. What was center fielder Devon White's batting average for the 1995 season he spent with the Blue Jays?

    a. .238
    b. .283
    c. .289
    d. .293

16. How many games did José Cruz play for the Blue Jays during the 2000 season?

    a. 99
    b. 106
    c. 142
    d. 162

17. How many times was former Blue Jays left fielder Shannon Stewart named to the MLB All-Star Game?

a. 0 times

b. 3 times

c. 6 times

d. 9 times

18. How many hits did left fielder George Bell collect during the nine seasons he spent with the Blue Jays?

a. 998

b. 1,001

c. 1,294

d. 1,501

19. How many home runs did former Blue Jays center fielder Lloyd Moseby hit in the MLB postseason in his career?

a. 0

b. 1

c. 3

d. 7

20. Rickey Henderson scored 37 runs in his 44 career games with the Blue Jays.

a. True

b. False

QUIZ ANSWERS

1. A – Oakland Athletics

2. B – False (3x All-Star)

3. C – 3

4. A – True

5. D – Detroit Tigers

6. B – 151

7. B – False [Blue Jays (10 years), Minnesota Twins (4 years), Oakland Athletics (1 year)]

8. B – 3

9. C – 4

10. D – 7

11. C – Boston Red Sox

12. A – True

13. B – 267

14. D – 57

15. B –.283

16. D – 162

17. A – 0 times

18. C – 1,294

19. B – 1

20. A – True

DID YOU KNOW?

1. Joe Carter played in three MLB postseasons with the Blue Jays from 1991-1993. He hit 6 home runs in 29 games played. He also played for the Cleveland Indians, San Diego Padres, San Francisco Giants, Chicago Cubs, and Baltimore Orioles.

2. Alex Rios played 809 games for the Toronto Blue Jays, the most of any team he played for in his 12-year MLB career. He also played for the Chicago White Sox, Texas Rangers, and Kansas City Royals.

3. Vernon Wells played 1,393 games for the Toronto Blue Jays, the most of any team he played for in his 15-year MLB career. He also played for the Los Angeles Angels of Anaheim and the New York Yankees.

4. Center fielder Colby Rasmus played four seasons for the Blue Jays. During those 4 seasons, he hit 66 home runs and played in 408 games. He also played for the St. Louis Cardinals, Houston Astros, Tampa Bay Rays, and Baltimore Orioles.

5. George Bell was named the 1987 AL MVP. He is also a 3x All-Star and 3x Silver Slugger Award winner. During his 12-year career, he played for the Blue Jays and both the Chicago White Sox and the Chicago Cubs.

6. Lloyd Moseby was a 1x All-Star and won one Silver Slugger Award in his career. In his 12-year career, he played for the Blue Jays and the Detroit Tigers.

7. Joe Carter was a 5x All-Star, a 2x Silver Slugger Award winner, and won two World Series championships in his career.

8. Rickey Henderson played for nine different MLB teams, including the Blue Jays. He had a 25-year long career, spending 14 of those years with the Oakland A's. Rickey also played for the San Diego Padres, New York Yankees, New York Mets, Boston Red Sox, Los Angeles Dodgers, Los Angeles Angels of Anaheim, and the Seattle Mariners.

9. Jose Canseco played for seven different MLB teams including the Blue Jays. He had a 17- year long career and spent nine years with the Oakland A's, but only one with the Blue Jays. He also played for the Texas Rangers, Boston Red Sox, Tampa Bay Devil Rays, New York Yankees and the Chicago White Sox.

10. Lourdes Gurriel Jr. hit 20 home runs for the Blue Jays during the 2019 season. He hit 11 the previous season.

CHAPTER 11:

INFIELDERS

QUIZ TIME!

1. How many games did former Blue Jays infielder Tony Fernández play in during his 12 seasons in Toronto?

    a. 1,101
    b. 1,280
    c. 1,450
    d. 1,90

2. Edwin Encarnacion was a 3x All-Star during his time with the Blue Jays.

    a. True
    b. False

3. How many home runs did former Blue Jays third baseman Josh Donaldson hit during his 2015 season in Toronto?

    a. 29
    b. 37
    c. 41
    d. 45

4. How many games did Troy Tulowitzki play in for the Blue Jays during the 2016 season?

    a. 41
    b. 66
    c. 101
    d. 131

5. Which MLB team did former Blue Jays infielder Aaron Hill NOT play for during his 13-season career?

    a. Arizona Diamondbacks
    b. Minnesota Twins
    c. Boston Red Sox
    d. San Francisco Giants

6. How many seasons did Paul Molitor play in the MLB?

    a. 12
    b. 15
    c. 18
    d. 21

7. Adam Lind played his entire MLB career with the Toronto Blue Jays.

    a. True
    b. False

8. Which MLB team did former Blue Jays infielder Joe Reyes NOT play for during his 16-season career?

    a. Boston Red Sox
    b. New York Mets
    c. Colorado Rockies
    d. Miami Marlins

9. What was Blue Jays second baseman Roberto Alomar's batting average during the 1993 World Series?

    a. .297
    b. .323
    c. .399
    d. .480

10. How many home runs did José Bautista hit for the Blue Jays during the 2010 season?

    a. 35
    b. 43
    c. 54
    d. 59

11. In what place did Blue Jays third baseman Vladimir Guerrero Jr. finish in the 2019 American League Rookie of the Year voting?

    a. 10th
    b. 6th
    c. 4th
    d. 2nd

12. Second baseman Roberto Alomar spent his entire 17-season career with the Toronto Blue Jays.

    a. True
    b. False

13. In what place did Cavan Biggio finish in the 2019 American League Rookie of the Year voting?

    a. 9th
    b. 7th

c. 5th

d. 2nd

14. Which team has former Blue Jays first baseman Justin Smoak NOT played for (as of the 2020 season) in his MLB career?

    a. Washington Nationals

    b. Seattle Mariners

    c. Texas Rangers

    d. Milwaukee Brewers

15. How many home runs did Munenori Kawasaki hit during his three seasons with the Blue Jays?

    a. 0

    b. 1

    c. 15

    d. 22

16. Tony Fernández was a 5x All-Star. In all but one of those All-Star Games, he represented the Blue Jays.

    a. True

    b. False

17. How many doubles did former Blue Jays first baseman John Olerud hit during his 1993 season with Toronto?

    a. 24

    b. 34

    c. 44

    d. 54

18. Former Blue Jays third baseman Brett Lawrie played in the MLB for six seasons. How many of those seasons did he spend with the Blue Jays?

    a. 3
    b. 4
    c. 5
    d. 6

19. How old was Vladimir Guerrero Jr. when he made his MLB debut with the Blue Jays in 2019?

    a. 19
    b. 20
    c. 21
    d. 22

20. Former Blue Jay Paul Molitor was named the 2017 American League Manager of the Year with the Minnesota Twins.

    a. True
    b. False

QUIZ ANSWERS

1. C – 1,450

2. A – True

3. C – 41

4. D – 131

5. B – Minnesota Twins

6. D – 21

7. B – False (Milwaukee Brewers, Seattle Mariners, Washington Nationals)

8. A – Boston Red Sox

9. D –.480

10. C – 54

11. B – 6th

12. B – False, San Diego Padres, Cleveland Indians, Baltimore Orioles, New York Mets, Chicago White Sox, Arizona Diamondbacks

13. C – 5th

14. A – Washington Nationals

15. B – 1

16. A – True

17. D – 54

18. B – 4

19. B – 20

20. A – True

DID YOU KNOW?

1. Former Blue Jay Paul Molitor was a 7x All-Star, won four Silver Slugger Awards, was a 1993 World Series Champion, was named World Series MVP, and is a Hall-of-Famer. He played three years in Toronto and 21 years in the MLB. He also played for the Milwaukee Brewers and the Minnesota Twins (a team he would later manage).

2. Blue Jays second baseman Roberto Alomar was a 12x All-Star, 10x Gold Glove Award winner, a 4x Silver Slugger Award winner, ALCS MVP, All-Star MVP, a 2x World Series Champion, and is a Hall-of-Famer. He was the first player to be inducted into the National Baseball Hall of Fame as a Blue Jay. Over the course of his 17-year career, he also played for the San Diego Padres, Cleveland Indians, Baltimore Orioles, New York Mets, Chicago White Sox, and the Arizona Diamondbacks.

3. Former Blue Jay Tony Fernández was a 5x All-Star, 4x Gold Glove Award winner, and a 1993 World Series Champion. He played for seven MLB teams in his 17-season career: the Blue Jays, San Diego Padres, New York Mets, Cleveland Indians, Cincinnati Reds, New York Yankees, and the Milwaukee Brewers. He passed away on February 16, 2020, at only 57 years old.

4. Former Blue Jay José Bautista was a 6x All-Star and 3x Silver Slugger Award winner. Although he played for

eight different MLB teams in his 15-season career, he was an All-Star only with the Blue Jays and he also won his Silver Slugger Awards as a Blue Jay. He also played for the Pittsburgh Pirates, Baltimore Orioles, Kansas City Royals, New York Mets, Tampa Bay Devil Rays, Philadelphia Phillies, and Atlanta Braves.

5. Former Blue Jays shortstop Troy Tulowitzki was a 5x All-Star, 2x Gold Glove Award winner, and a 2x Silver Slugger Award winner. However, most of this success came during his time spent with the Colorado Rockies. Much of his career was plagued by injury. In his 13 years spent in the MLB, he played for the Rockies (10 years), Blue Jays (3 years), and the New York Yankees (1 season and only 5 games).

6. Blue Jays' second baseman Cavan Biggio is the son of former MLB star and Hall-of-Famer, Craig Biggio. Blue Jays' third baseman Vladimir Guerrero Jr. is the son of former MLB star and Hall-of-Famer, Vladimir Guerrero. Blue Jays' shortstop Bo Bichette is the son of former MLB outfielder Dante Bichette (who is also currently a Blue Jays coach). Blue Jays first baseman Travis Shaw is the son of former MLB pitcher Jeff Shaw. The entire Blue Jays infield consists of 2nd-generation MLB players. This is just the second time in MLB history this has happened.

7. Current Blue Jay Joe Panik won a World Series Championship with the San Francisco Giants in 2014. So far in his career, he has played for the Jays, Giants, and the New York Mets.

8. Former Blue Jay Edwin Encarnacion spent eight years in Toronto. He hit 239 home runs in 999 games played for the Blue Jays. He has also played for the Cincinnati Reds, Cleveland Indians, New York Yankees, Seattle Mariners, and the Chicago White Sox so far in his career.

9. Former Blue Jays infielder Marco Scutaro won NLCS MVP and a World Series championship in 2012 with the San Francisco Giants. During his 13-year career, he played for the Blue Jays, Giants, the Oakland A's, New York Mets, Boston Red Sox, and the Colorado Rockies.

10. Former Blue Jay José Bautista won the 2010 and 2011 American League Hank Aaron Award. This award is given each season to the best hitter in each league.

CHAPTER 12:

PITCHERS AND CATCHERS

QUIZ TIME!

1. What was Roger Clemens' ERA during his 1997 season with the Blue Jays?

   a. 1.93
   b. 2.05
   c. 2.62
   d. 2.85

2. The most home runs that catcher Russell Martin hit in a single season with the Blue Jays is 23.

   a. True
   b. False

3. Which MLB team did former Blue Jay R.A. Dickey NOT pitch for during his 15-season career?

   a. Texas Rangers
   b. Seattle Mariners
   c. New York Mets
   d. San Diego Padres

4. Which Blue Jays manager was a catcher during his playing career?

    a. Bobby Cox

    b. John Gibbons

    c. Cito Gaston

    d. Charlie Montoyo

5. How many wins did pitcher Roy Halladay collect for the Blue Jays in 2003?

    a. 14

    b. 18

    c. 22

    d. 25

6. How many saves did Ken Giles record for the Blue Jays during the 2019 season?

    a. 12

    b. 14

    c. 23

    d. 34

7. Former Blue Jays catcher Gregg Zaun was never named to an MLB All-Star Game.

    a. True

    b. False

8. Former Blue Jays pitcher Jimmy Key led the AL in ERA in which season?

    a. 1984

    b. 1985

c. 1986

d. 1987

9. How many strikeouts did A.J. Burnett record with the Blue Jays in 2008?

    a. 128

    b. 201

    c. 231

    d. 289

10. What year did former Blue Jays pitcher Pat Hentgen win the AL Cy Young Award?

    a. 1993

    b. 1996

    c. 1997

    d. 1999

11. What was J.A. Happ's ERA for his 2016 season with the Blue Jays?

    a. 1.85

    b. 2.69

    c. 3.03

    d. 3.18

12. Catcher Buck Martinez spent his entire 17-year MLB career with the Toronto Blue Jays.

    a. True

    b. False

13. What year did former Blue Jays pitcher Marcus Stroman win his first Gold Glove Award?

a. 2015

b. 2017

c. 2018

d. 2019

14. How many All-Star Games was former Blue Jays pitcher David Wells named to over the course of his 21-season career?

a. 3

b. 9

c. 12

d. 18

15. What year was pitcher Brett Cecil named to the MLB All-Star Game as a member of the Blue Jays?

a. 2009

b. 2011

c. 2013

d. 2016

16. Former Blue Jays catcher Pat Borders was named the 1992 World Series MVP.

a. True

b. False

17. During his 16-year MLB career, pitcher Mark Buehrle played for the Blue Jays, Chicago White Sox, and who else?

a. Cleveland Indians

b. Los Angeles Dodgers

c. Oakland Athletics

d. Miami Marlins

18. During his 15-year MLB career, pitcher Chris Carpenter played for the Blue Jays and what other team?

   a. St. Louis Cardinals

   b. Texas Rangers

   c. Kansas City Royals

   d. Seattle Mariners

19. How many wild pitches did pitcher Mike Timlin throw in his 1991 rookie season with the Blue Jays?

   a. 0

   b. 1

   c. 3

   d. 5

20. Former Blue Jays catcher Bengie Molina is the brother of Yadier and José Molina, both also MLB catchers.

   a. True

   b. False

QUIZ ANSWERS

1. B – 2.05
2. A – True
3. D – San Diego Padres
4. B – John Gibbons
5. C – 22
6. C – 23
7. A – True
8. D – 1987
9. C – 231
10. B – 1996
11. D – 3.18
12. B – False, Blue Jays, Kansas City Royals, Milwaukee Brewers
13. B – 2017
14. A – 3
15. C – 2013
16. A – True
17. D – Miami Marlins
18. A – St. Louis Cardinals
19. D – 5
20. A – True

DID YOU KNOW?

1. Former Blue Jays pitcher David Wells spent eight years in Toronto out of his 21-year MLB career. He also played for the New York Yankees, San Diego Padres, Detroit Tigers, Boston Red Sox, Los Angeles Dodgers, Cincinnati Reds, Baltimore Orioles, and Chicago White Sox.

2. Hall-of-Famer Roy Halladay was a 2x Cy Young Award winner (2003 and 2010) and an 8x All-Star.

3. Former Blue Jays pitcher Roger Clemens was an MVP, 7x Cy Young Award winner, 2x Pitching Triple Crown winner, 11x All-Star, 2x World Series Champion, 7x ERA title winner, and All-Star MVP.

4. Former Blue Jays pitcher Dave Stieb was a 7x All-Star and ERA title winner. He also threw the first no-hitter in Blue Jays history.

5. Former Blue Jays catcher Ernie Whitt played 12 out of his 15 seasons in the MLB in Toronto. He also played for the Atlanta Braves, Boston Red Sox, and Baltimore Orioles.

6. No pitcher has ever thrown a perfect game for the Blue Jays (as of the 2019 season).

7. Star pitcher David Price spent one season with the Blue Jays in 2015. His record was 9-1 with a 2.30 ERA and 87 strikeouts.

8. Former Blue Jays pitcher Jimmy Key was a 5x All-Star, 2x World Series Champion, and ERA title winner.

9. R.A. Dickey's record with the Blue Jays was identical in 2013 and 2014. Both years he went 14-13 with 34 games started. He won a Gold Glove in 2013 as well.

10. Pat Hentgen was a Cy Young Award winner, 3x All-Star, and won a 1993 World Series championship with Toronto.

CHAPTER 13:

WORLD SERIES

QUIZ TIME!

1. How many World Series have the Toronto Blue Jays won?

    a. 0

    b. 1

    c. 2

    d. 4

2. How many AL Pennants have the Toronto Blue Jays won?

    a. 0

    b. 1

    c. 2

    d. 3

3. Which team did the Toronto Blue Jays face in the 1992 World Series?

    a. New York Mets

    b. Atlanta Braves

    c. Los Angeles Dodgers

    d. Florida Marlins

4. Which team did the Toronto Blue Jays face in the 1993 World Series?

    a. Atlanta Braves
    b. Montreal Expos
    c. Houston Astros
    d. Philadelphia Phillies

5. Who was the Blue Jays' manager during BOTH of their World Series wins (1992, 1993)?

    a. Bobby Cox
    b. Cito Gaston
    c. Jim Fregosi
    d. John Gibbons

6. How many games did the 1992 World Series go?

    a. 4
    b. 5
    c. 6
    d. 7

7. Pat Borders was named the 1992 World Series MVP.

    a. True
    b. False

8. Which Blue Jays player was named the 1993 World Series MVP?

    a. Paul Molitor
    b. Roberto Alomar
    c. Joe Carter
    d. Rickey Henderson

9. How many games did the 1993 World Series go?

    a. 4

    b. 5

    c. 6

    d. 7

10. Which pitcher started Game 1 of the 1992 World Series for the Blue Jays?

    a. Al Leiter

    b. Jack Morris

    c. Dave Stieb

    d. Jimmy Key

11. Which pitcher started Game 1 of the 1993 World Series for the Blue Jays?

    a. Al Leiter

    b. Jack Morris

    c. Dave Stieb

    d. Jimmy Key

12. Mike Timlin was awarded the save in Game 6 of the 1992 World Series.

    a. True

    b. False

13. Which Blue Jay hit the most home runs in the 1992 World Series?

    a. Roberto Alomar

    b. Pat Borders

    c. Joe Carter

    d. Candy Maldonado

14. What was Paul Molitor's batting average for the 1993 World Series?

    a. .301
    b. .399
    c. .480
    d. .500

15. Which Blue Jay did NOT hit a home run in the 1993 World Series?

    a. John Olerud
    b. Devon White
    c. Roberto Alomar
    d. Joe Carter

16. The Toronto Blue Jays won their first and only wild card berth in 2016.

    a. True
    b. False

17. Which team did the Toronto Blue Jays beat in the 1992 ALCS to advance to the World Series?

    a. California Angels
    b. Oakland Athletics
    c. Detroit Tigers
    d. Minnesota Twins

18. Which team did the Toronto Blue Jays beat in the 1993 ALCS to advance to the World Series?

    a. New York Yankees
    b. Boston Red Sox

c. Oakland Athletics

d. Chicago White Sox

19. What was the final score of Game 6 of the 1992 World Series?

   a. Blue Jays 10, Braves 9

   b. Blue Jays 5, Braves 4

   c. Blue Jays 4, Braves 3

   d. Blue Jays 1, Braves 0

20. What was the final score of Game 6 of the 1993 World Series?

   a. Blue Jays 8, Phillies 6

   b. Blue Jays 6, Phillies 4

   c. Blue Jays 11, Phillies 9

   d. Blue Jays 2, Phillies 0

QUIZ ANSWERS

1. C – 2

2. C – 2

3. B – Atlanta Braves

4. D – Philadelphia Phillies

5. B – Cito Gaston

6. C – 6

7. A – True

8. A – Paul Molitor

9. C – 6

10. B – Jack Morris

11. A – Al Leiter

12. A – True

13. C – Joe Carter (2)

14. D –.500

15. C – Roberto Alomar

16. A – True

17. B – Oakland Athletics

18. D – Chicago White Sox

19. C – Blue Jays 4, Braves 3

20. A – Blue Jays 8, Phillies 6

DID YOU KNOW?

1. The Blue Jays beat two National League East teams, the Braves and Phillies, to win their World Series championships.

2. Both of the Blue Jays' World Series championships went to 6 games each.

3. Pat Borders had the most hits for the Blue Jays in the 1992 World Series with 9. Paul Molitor and Roberto Alomar tied for the most hits for the Blue Jays in the 1993 World Series with 12 each.

4. Tom Henke collected 2 saves for the Blue Jays in the 1992 World Series and Mike Timlin collected 1 save. Duane Ward had 2 saves for the Blue Jays in the 1993 World Series.

5. Jack Morris led Blue Jays pitchers in the 1992 World Series with 12 strikeouts. Juan Guzman struck out the most batters out of all Blue Jays pitchers in the 1993 World Series, also with 12.

6. Roberto Alomar scored the most runs for the Blue Jays in the 1992 World Series with 3. Paul Molitor scored the most runs for the Blue Jays in the 1993 World Series with 10.

7. Game 1 of the 1992 World Series was played at Atlanta-Fulton County Stadium. President Jimmy Carter threw out the first pitch, Billy Ray Cyrus sang the National Anthem, and Michael Burgess sang the Canadian Anthem.

8. Game 6 of the 1992 World Series took place at Atlanta-Fulton County Stadium. Harry Connick Jr. sang the National Anthem and The Nylons sang the Canadian Anthem.

9. Game 1 of the 1993 World Series took place at the SkyDome in Toronto. Hall-of-Famer George Brett threw out the first pitch, "The Queen of Soul" Aretha Franklin sang the National Anthem, and Michael Burgess once again sang the Canadian Anthem.

10. Game 6 of the 1993 World Series is better known as "The Joe Carter Walk-Off Game." "Touch 'em all, Joe! You'll never hit a bigger home run in your life!"

CHAPTER 14:

HEATED RIVALRIES

QUIZ TIME!

1. Which team does NOT play in the American League East with the Blue Jays?

    a. Boston Red Sox

    b. Washington Nationals

    c. Baltimore Orioles

    d. Tampa Bay Rays

2. The Blue Jays and Orioles are the only two teams in the AL East with birds as their mascot.

    a. True

    b. False

3. A rivalry began with the Texas Rangers after José Bautista's dramatic bat flip in which year?

    a. 2012

    b. 2013

    c. 2015

    d. 2016

4. The Blue Jays have won two World Series championships. How many have the Texas Rangers won?

    a. 0

    b. 1

    c. 3

    d. 6

5. The Blue Jays have two World Series championships. How many do the Baltimore Orioles have?

    a. 0

    b. 2

    c. 3

    d. 7

6. The Blue Jays have won two World Series championships. How many have the New York Yankees won?

    a. 10

    b. 14

    c. 20

    d. 27

7. The Blue Jays have the most AL East Championships of any team in the division.

    a. True

    b. False

8. Which player has NOT played for both the Rays and the Blue Jays?

    a. David Price

    b. José Bautista

c. Eric Sogard

d. Carlos Delgado

9. Which player has NOT played for both the Red Sox and the Blue Jays?

   a. Jose Canseco

   b. George Bell

   c. Rajai Davis

   d. Aaron Hill

10. Which player has NOT played for both the Orioles and the Blue Jays?

   a. Adam Lind

   b. Roberto Alomar

   c. Joe Carter

   d. Jimmy Key

11. Which player has NOT played for both the Yankees and the Blue Jays?

   a. Jesse Barfield

   b. Tony Fernández

   c. Carlos Delgado

   d. Edwin Encarnacion

12. When the Blue Jays and Montreal Expos played a series together, the winner of the series was awarded the Pearson Cup.

   a. True

   b. False

13. Where is the Pearson Cup now on display?

    a. National Baseball Hall of Fame
    b. Canadian Baseball Hall of Fame
    c. Rogers Centre
    d. Nationals Park

14. How many times did the Blue Jays play the Montreal Expos?

    a. 29
    b. 37
    c. 43
    d. 56

15. As of the end of the 2019 season, the last time the Blue Jays won the division was 2015. When was the last time the Tampa Bay Rays won the division?

    a. 2010
    b. 2011
    c. 2013
    d. 2016

16. The Montreal Expos won ONE National League East title, in 1981.

    a. True
    b. False

17. As of the end of the 2019 season, the last time the Blue Jays won the division was 2015. When was the last time the Baltimore Orioles won the division?

    a. 2012
    b. 2013

c. 2014

d. 2018

18. Which fellow American League East team did the Toronto Blue Jays play in the 2016 AL wild-card game?

    a. Tampa Bay Rays

    b. New York Yankees

    c. Boston Red Sox

    d. Baltimore Orioles

19. Who threw the ceremonial first pitch before the 2016 American League wild-card game?

    a. Joe Carter

    b. Roberto Alomar

    c. Gregg Zaun

    d. Jimmy Key

20. Before the 2014 season, the Blue Jays and New York Mets closed out spring training with a two-game exhibition series at Olympic Stadium, where their past rival, the Montreal Expos played. It is now a yearly tradition to play two exhibition games there.

    a. True

    b. False

QUIZ ANSWERS

1. B – Washington Nationals

2. A – True

3. C – 2015

4. A – 0

5. C – 3

6. D – 27

7. B – False (Yankees)

8. D – Carlos Delgado

9. B – George Bell

10. A – Adam Lind

11. C – Carlos Delgado

12. A – True

13. B – Canadian Baseball Hall of Fame

14. C – 43

15. A – 2010

16. A – True

17. C – 2014

18. D – Baltimore Orioles

19. B – Roberto Alomar

20. A – True

DID YOU KNOW?

1. The Cleveland Indians, Detroit Tigers, Milwaukee Brewers, and Washington Senators used to be members of the American League East.

2. The New York Yankees, Boston Red Sox, and Baltimore Orioles are all founding members of the American League East. The Blue Jays joined the division in 1977 and Tampa Bay joined in 1998 as the Devil Rays.

3. The 2016 American League wild-card game was the first postseason meeting between the two teams.

4. In the 2016 American League wild card, game, the Blue Jays defeated the Baltimore Orioles 5-2 in extra innings. Edwin Encarnacion hit a walk-off three-run home run off Ubaldo Jiménez. Orioles closer and 2016 AL Reliever of the Year, Zach Britton, controversially did not pitch in the game. Encarnacion was only the fourth player in MLB history to hit a walk-off home run in a winner-take-all postseason game.

5. The Blue Jays and Baltimore Orioles had identical regular-season records during the 2016 season, 89-73.

6. The New York Yankees have won the AL East 19 times, the Boston Red Sox have won the division 10 times, the Baltimore Orioles have won 9 times, the Blue Jays have won 6 times, and the Tampa Bay Rays have won the AL East twice.

7. "He got me pretty good, so I have to give him that. But it takes a little bit of a bigger man to knock me down." – José Bautista on Rougned Odor after their on-field brawl following Bautista's postseason bat flip.

8. A.J Burnett, Melky Cabrera, Jose Canseco, Roger Clemens, Phil Coke, Tyler Clippard, A.J. Cole, Octavio Dotel, Cecil Fielder, Curtis Granderson, Rickey Henderson, Jimmy Key, Al Leiter, Russell Martin, Troy Tulowitzki, David Wells, Vernon Wells, and Dave Winfield all played for both the Blue Jays and the New York Yankees.

9. Clay Buchholz, Jose Canseco, Roger Clemens, Rajai Davis, Rickey Henderson, Aaron Hill, Eric Hinske, Bobby Kielty, Kevin Millar, John Olerud, Kevin Pillar, David Price, Jarrod Saltalamacchia, Marco Scutaro, Matt Stairs, Mike Timlin, and Ernie Whitt all played for both the Blue Jays and the Boston Red Sox.

10. Roberto Alomar, José Bautista, Joe Carter, Scott Feldman, Juan Guzman, LaTroy Hawkins, Pat Hentgen, Cesar Izturis, Edwin Jackson, Jimmy Key, Kevin Millar, Colby Rasmus, Mike Timlin, David Wells, Ernie Whitt, and Gregg Zaun all played for both the Blue Jays and the Baltimore Orioles.

CHAPTER 15:

THE AWARDS SECTION

QUIZ TIME!

1. Which Blue Jays pitcher won an American League Cy Young Award in 2003?

   a. Pat Hentgen
   b. Roy Halladay
   c. Roger Clemens
   d. Marcus Stroman

2. No Blue Jays catcher or first baseman has ever won an American League Gold Glove Award.

   a. True
   b. False

3. Which Blue Jays player won the American League MVP Award in 2015?

   a. José Reyes
   b. Edwin Encarnacion
   c. José Bautista
   d. Josh Donaldson

4. Which Blue Jay most recently won the AL Rookie of the Year Award (as of the 2019 season)?

   a. Alfredo Griffin
   b. Eric Hinske
   c. José Bautista
   d. Edwin Encarnacion

5. How many Gold Glove Awards did Roberto Alomar win during his time as a Blue Jay?

   a. 2
   b. 3
   c. 5
   d. 8

6. Who are the only two pitchers in Blue Jays franchise history to win an American League Gold Glove Award?

   a. R.A. Dickey and Roy Halladay
   b. Roy Halladay and Marcus Stroman
   c. R.A. Dickey and Marcus Stroman
   d. Dave Stieb and Roy Halladay

7. No Blue Jays manager has ever won an American League Manager of the Year Award.

   a. True
   b. False

8. Which Blue Jays player was named the DHL Hometown Hero? (Voted by MLB fans as the most outstanding player in franchise history.)

   a. Roy Halladay
   b. Joe Carter

    c. Roberto Alomar

    d. Carlos Delgado

9. Which former Blue Jay was named the World Baseball Classic MVP in 2017?

    a. Troy Tulowitzki

    b. Kevin Pillar

    c. José Bautista

    d. Marcus Stroman

10. Which former Blue Jay was the American League home run leader in 1986?

    a. Jesse Barfield

    b. George Bell

    c. Lloyd Moseby

    d. Ernie Whitt

11. Which Blue Jay was named the Wilson MLB Defensive Player of the Year in 2015?

    a. Josh Donaldson

    b. Justin Smoak

    c. Kevin Pillar

    d. Russell Martin

12. Vernon Wells NEVER won a Silver Slugger Award during his career with the Blue Jays.

    a. True

    b. False

13. Which Blue Jay did NOT win an AL Hank Aaron Award during his time in Toronto?

a. Carlos Delgado

b. José Bautista

c. Josh Donaldson

d. Paul Molitor

14. Which Blue Jay was named the ALCS MVP in 1993?

a. Dave Stewart

b. Rickey Henderson

c. Paul Molitor

d. Roberto Alomar

15. Who is the only Blue Jay to ever win an AL Comeback Player of the Year Award in franchise history?

a. Roy Halladay

b. Vernon Wells

c. Aaron Hill

d. R.A. Dickey

16. No Blue Jays player has ever WON the Home Run Derby.

a. True

b. False

17. Which Blue Jay was named the 1992 World Series MVP?

a. Joe Carter

b. Pat Borders

c. Roberto Alomar

d. Dave Winfield

18. Which Blue Jay was named the 1993 World Series MVP?

a. Pat Borders

b. Paul Molitor

c. Rickey Henderson

d. Dave Stewart

19. Which former Blue Jay was named the American League MVP in 1987?

    a. Jesse Barfield

    b. Lloyd Moseby

    c. Fred McGriff

    d. George Bell

20. Former Blue Jay Alfredo Griffin was named the American League Rookie of the Year in 1979.

    a. True

    b. False

QUIZ ANSWERS

1. B – Roy Halladay

2. A – True

3. D – Josh Donaldson

4. B – Eric Hinske (2002)

5. C – 5

6. C – R. A Dickey (2013) and Marcus Stroman (2017)

7. B – False, Bobby Cox (1985)

8. B – Joe Carter

9. D – Marcus Stroman

10. A – Jesse Barfield (40)

11. C – Kevin Pillar

12. B – False, 2003

13. D – Paul Molitor

14. A – Dave Stewart

15. C – Aaron Hill (2009)

16. A – True

17. Pat Borders

18. B – Paul Molitor

19. D – George Bell

20. A – True

DID YOU KNOW?

1. Roger Clemens won two AL Cy Young Awards in a row with the Blue Jays in 1997 and 1998.

2. No Blue Jays catcher or shortstop has ever won an AL Silver Slugger Award.

3. In 1994, the 1993 Blue Jays won an ESPN ESPY Award for "Outstanding Team."

4. The Neil McCarl Award is presented by the Baseball Writers Association of America (BBWAA) to the Toronto Blue Jays Player of the Year. Carlos Delgado has won the most Neil McCarl Awards so far, with six.

5. Roger Clemens won two MLB Pitching Triple Crowns during his time in Toronto. In 1997 and 1998, he was the MLB leader in ERA, wins, and strikeouts.

6. The Blue Jays have had the oldest player in the American League on their team four times: Phil Niekro in 1987, Omar Vizquel in 2012, LaTroy Hawkins in 2015, and R.A. Dickey in 2016.

7. Three Blue Jays have won the American League Edgar Martínez Award as the league's most outstanding designated hitter. Dave Winfield was honored with the award in 1992, Paul Molitor won in it 1993, and Adam Lind won it in 2009.

8. The Blue Jays as a team won the Wilson Defensive Team of the Year Award in both 2012 and 2013.

9. Although Cito Gaston is the Blue Jays' all-time winningest manager, he never won an AL Manager of the Year Award during his time in Toronto.

10. The first Blue Jays players to win a Gold Glove Award were Tony Fernández and Jesse Barfield in 1986.

CHAPTER 16:

THE SIX

QUIZ TIME!

1. Hanlan's Point Stadium in Centre Island is where which player hit his first professional home run?

    a. Hank Aaron

    b. Willie Mays

    c. Babe Ruth

    d. Jackie Robinson

2. Toronto is the only Canadian city with seven professional sports teams.

    a. True

    b. False

3. What percent of Hollywood movies are filmed in Toronto?

    a. 10

    b. 20

    c. 25

    d. 40

4. What was the Toronto International Film Festival originally called?

    a. Toronto Movie Festival
    b. Canadian International Film Festival
    c. Canada Movie Fest
    d. The Festival of Festivals

5. Toronto is the capital of which province?

    a. Alberta
    b. Ontario
    c. Nova Scotia
    d. Manitoba

6. How many outdoor skating rinks are there in Toronto?

    a. 0
    b. 22
    c. 39
    d. 52

7. Rogers Centre was the first stadium in the world to have a fully retractable roof.

    a. True
    b. False

8. Which famous rapper nicknamed Toronto "The Six"?

    a. Quavo
    b. Drake
    c. Jay-Z
    d. Eminem

9. What is the name of Toronto's NHL team?

   a. Toronto Sharks

   b. Toronto Wild

   c. Toronto Blue Jackets

   d. Toronto Maple Leafs

10. What is the name of Toronto's NBA team?

   a. Toronto Heat

   b. Toronto Pelicans

   c. Toronto Raptors

   d. Toronto Pistons

11. What is the name of Toronto's MLS team?

   a. Toronto FC

   b. Toronto Earthquakes

   c. Toronto United

   d. Toronto Dynamo

12. The whoopee cushion was invented in Toronto.

   a. True

   b. False

13. There are over how many library branches across the city of Toronto?

   a. 20

   b. 50

   c. 80

   d. 100

14. Toronto is the _____ largest city in North America.

   a. 2nd
   b. 5th
   c. 8th
   d. 12th

15. What is the name of the arena that the Toronto Raptors of the NBA and the Toronto Maple Leafs of the NHL call home?

   a. Pepsi Center
   b. Chase Center
   c. United Center
   d. Scotiabank Arena

16. What is the name of the stadium that the Toronto FC of the MLS calls home?

   a. BMO Field
   b. Providence Park
   c. Exploria Stadium
   d. BC Place

17. What parade in Toronto is the longest parade in North America?

   a. Torchlight Procession
   b. Mardi Gras
   c. Caribana
   d. Rose

18. Toronto's Pearson Airport is the largest airport in Canada. What is the Pearson Airport's code?

a. TPP

b. TOR

c. TPA

d. YYZ

19. Toronto has over how many restaurants?

    a. 2,000

    b. 4,000

    c. 8,000

    d. 10,000

20. Toronto was once called "York, Upper Canada."

    a. True

    b. False

QUIZ ANSWERS

1. C – Babe Ruth

2. A – True

3. C – 25

4. D – The Festival of Festivals

5. B – Ontario

6. D – 52

7. A – True

8. B – Drake

9. D – Toronto Maple Leafs

10. C – Toronto Raptors

11. A – Toronto FC

12. A – True

13. D – 100

14. B – 5th

15. D – Scotiabank Arena

16. A – BMO Field

17. C – Caribana

18. D – YYZ

19. C – 8,000

20. A – True

DID YOU KNOW?

1. The Toronto Zoo is the largest zoo in Canada.

2. People have lived in Toronto since shortly after the last Ice Age.

3. The CN Tower was once the tallest free-standing structure in the world. It held that title for 34 years. The CN Tower is 553.3 meters high.

4. Ripley's Aquarium has 1.5 million gallons of marine and freshwater habitats. It has over 20,000 specimens from over 450 species.

5. The Royal Ontario Museum is the largest and the most visited museum in Canada.

6. Toronto attracts over 25 million tourists every year.

7. Toronto has an extremely low crime rate and is known as one of the safest major cities in North America.

8. Toronto has more than 1,800 buildings that are higher than 98 feet.

9. Over 100 languages are spoken in Toronto. With over 2.5 million residents, it has the largest population in Canada.

10. Yonge Street is one of the longest streets in the world at 1,896 km.

CHAPTER 17:

ROBBIE

QUIZ TIME!

1. Where was Roberto Alomar born?

    a. San Juan, Puerto Rico

    b. Miami, Florida

    c. Ponce, Puerto Rico

    d. Havana, Cuba

2. Roberto Alomar was a switch hitter.

    a. True

    b. False

3. Roberto Alomar played for the Toronto Blue Jays for five seasons. He also played for six other MLB teams. Which of the teams below did he NOT play for during his 17-season MLB career?

    a. San Diego Padres

    b. Arizona Diamondbacks

    c. Los Angeles Dodgers

    d. Baltimore Orioles

4. What year was Roberto Alomar born?

    a. 1968
    b. 1969
    c. 1970
    d. 1975

5. What uniform number did Roberto Alomar wear as a member of the Blue Jays?

    a. 2
    b. 12
    c. 22
    d. 21

6. How many home runs did Roberto Alomar hit during his career?

    a. 198
    b. 201
    c. 210
    d. 211

7. Sandy Alomar Jr. is Roberto Alomar's brother.

    a. True
    b. False

8. What year did Roberto Alomar make his MLB debut with the Padres?

    a. 1987
    b. 1988
    c. 1989
    d. 1990

9. Where did Roberto Alomar attend high school?

    a. Eugenio Guerra Cruz High School
    b. Superior Urbana High School
    c. Stella Marquez High School
    d. Luis Munoz Rivera High School

10. How many All-Star Games was Roberto Alomar named to in his 17-year MLB career?

    a. 8
    b. 10
    c. 12
    d. 15

11. How many Gold Glove Awards did Roberto Alomar win?

    a. 9
    b. 10
    c. 11
    d. 12

12. Roberto Alomar NEVER won a World Series championship.

    a. True
    b. False

13. What year was Roberto Alomar inducted into the National Baseball Hall of Fame with 90% of the vote?

    a. 2009
    b. 2010
    c. 2011
    d. 2012

14. What year was Roberto Alomar named the MVP of the All-Star Game MVP?

    a. 1992
    b. 1993
    c. 1996
    d. 1998

15. How many Silver Slugger Awards did Roberto Alomar win?

    a. 4
    b. 3
    c. 2
    d. 1

16. Roberto Alomar currently serves as a special assistant to the Blue Jays organization.

    a. True
    b. False

17. How many times was Roberto Alomar named the Toronto Blue Jays' Player of the Year?

    a. Once
    b. Twice
    c. Three times
    d. Five times

18. What year was Roberto Alomar named ALCS MVP?

    a. 1991
    b. 1992
    c. 1993
    d. 1995

19. Alomar's game-tying home run in Game 4 of the 1992 _____ is widely considered the most important hit in Blue Jays history.

    a. Wild card round
    b. ALDS
    c. ALCS
    d. World Series

20. Roberto Alomar was the first player to go into the National Baseball Hall of Fame depicted as a Blue Jay on his plaque.

    a. True
    b. False

QUIZ ANSWERS

1. C – Ponce, Puerto Rico

2. A – True

3. C – Los Angeles Dodgers

4. A – 1968

5. B – 12

6. C – 210

7. A – True

8. B – 1988

9. D – Luis Munoz Rivera High School

10. C – 12

11. B – 10

12. B – False, 1992 and 1993 with the Blue Jays

13. C – 2011

14. D – 1998

15. A – 4

16. A – True

17. C – Three times

18. B – 1992

19. C – ALCS

20. A – True

DID YOU KNOW?

1. Roberto Alomar played for seven MLB teams in his 17-season MLB career: the Blue Jays, the San Diego Padres, the Cleveland Indians, the Baltimore Orioles, the New York Mets, the Chicago White Sox, and the Arizona Diamondbacks.

2. Roberto and his brother Sandy Alomar, Jr. were teammates with three different teams: the Padres, Indians, and White Sox. They also both played for the Mets, but not at the same time.

3. Roberto Alomar became only the third Puerto Rican to be elected to the National Baseball Hall of Fame after Roberto Clemente and Orlando Cepeda. Following Alomar's election, Ivan Rodriguez and Edgar Martínez have also been elected to the Hall.

4. In each of his five seasons spent with the Blue Jays, Alomar was named to the MLB All-Star Game and won a Gold Glove Award.

5. When Roberto and his brother Sandy Jr. were on summer vacation from school, they would spend time with their dad in the New York Yankees clubhouse shagging balls hit by the likes of Thurman Munson and Graig Nettles.

6. Roberto's father, Sandy Alomar Sr., played for the Milwaukee/Atlanta Braves, California Angels, New York

Yankees, Chicago White Sox, Texas Rangers, and New York Mets.

7. On Opening Day in 2008, Roberto Alomar was inducted into the Blue Jays' Level of Excellence at Rogers Centre. His number was retired by the Blue Jays in 2011. He became the first Blue Jay to have his uniform number retired by the team.

8. In 2010, Roberto Alomar was elected to the Canadian Baseball Hall of Fame.

9. In 2011, Roberto Alomar was elected to the Caribbean Baseball Hall of Fame.

10. Roberto Alomar holds the MLB record for most Gold Glove Awards for a second baseman, with 10.

CHAPTER 18:

SIR DAVID

QUIZ TIME!

1. Where was Dave Stieb born?

    a. Sioux Falls, South Dakota

    b. Milwaukee, Wisconsin

    c. Dallas, Texas

    d. Santa Ana, California

2. Stieb won 140 games in the 1980s. This was the second-highest total by a pitcher in that decade, behind only Jack Morris.

    a. True

    b. False

3. Dave Stieb played for two MLB teams over the course of his career; the Blue Jays and the _____.

    a. Milwaukee Brewers

    b. Chicago White Sox

    c. San Francisco Giants

    d. New York Mets

4. When was Dave Stieb born?

    a. June 22, 1955
    b. June 22, 1957
    c. July 22, 1957
    d. July 22, 1955

5. How many MLB All-Star Games was Dave Stieb named to over the course of his career?

    a. 3
    b. 6
    c. 7
    d. 10

6. What year did Dave Stieb win the American League ERA title with an ERA of 2.48?

    a. 1983
    b. 1985
    c. 1992
    d. 1998

7. Dave Stieb played for the White Sox in 1993, then did not play in the majors from 1994 through 1997. He finished his career with the Blue Jays in 1998 at 40 years of age.

    a. True
    b. False

8. Where did Dave Stieb attend college?

    a. Cal State Fullerton
    b. Chapman University
    c. The University of Chicago
    d. Southern Illinois University Carbondale

9. What year did Dave Stieb make his MLB debut with the Blue Jays?

   a. 1978
   b. 1979
   c. 1980
   d. 1981

10. How many strikeouts did Dave Stieb collect during his 16-year career?

   a. 1,304
   b. 1,538
   c. 1,669
   d. 1,996

11. How many saves did Dave Stieb collect during his career?

   a. 0
   b. 1
   c. 3
   d. 8

12. Dave Stieb signed as a free agent with the Kansas City Royals in 1993 but was released by them a little over a month later.

   a. True
   b. False

13. What date did Dave Stieb pitch his no-hitter?

   a. August 2, 1991
   b. August 2, 1990
   c. September 2, 1991
   d. September 2, 1990

14. What year was Dave Stieb inducted into the Canadian Baseball Hall of Fame?

   a. 2002
   b. 2004
   c. 2005
   d. 2007

15. What year did Dave Stieb win *The Sporting News'* Pitcher of the Year Award?

   a. 1981
   b. 1982
   c. 1992
   d. 1998

16. Dave Stieb was drafted by the Toronto Blue Jays.

   a. True
   b. False

17. How old was Dave Stieb when he made his MLB debut with the Blue Jays?

   a. 19
   b. 20
   c. 21
   d. 22

18. Where did Dave Stieb attend high school?

   a. Oak Grove High School
   b. Silver Creek High School
   c. Pioneer High School
   d. Willow Glen High School

19. The Blue Jays gave away a _____ to fans to celebrate the 20th anniversary of Dave Stieb's no-hitter.

   a. Blanket
   b. Bobblehead
   c. Poster
   d. Beer mug

20. Dave Stieb was the first Blue Jays pitcher to start an MLB All-Star Game.

   a. True
   b. False

QUIZ ANSWERS

1. D – Santa Ana, California

2. A – True

3. B – Chicago White Sox

4. C – July 22, 1957

5. C – 7

6. B – 1985

7. A – True

8. D – Southern Illinois University Carbondale

9. B – 1979

10. C – 1,669

11. C – 3

12. A – True

13. D – September 2, 1990

14. C – 2005

15. B – 1982

16. A – True

17. C – 21

18. A – Oak Grove High School

19. B – Bobblehead

20. A – True

DID YOU KNOW?

1. Dave Stieb is a member of the Toronto Blue Jays' Level of Excellence at Rogers Centre along with Tony Fernández, George Bell, Roberto Alomar, Carlos Delgado, Joe Carter, Cito Gaston, Tom Cheek, Paul Beeston, Roy Halladay, and Pat Gillick.

2. On August 29, 2010, Stieb threw the ceremonial first pitch at the Rogers Centre, celebrating the 20th anniversary of his no-hitter. Stieb's number 37 was engraved on the pitcher's mound for the game.

3. After retirement, Stieb moved to Reno, Nevada, where he took up the electric guitar as a hobby and works as a building contractor.

4. Dave Stieb's younger brother, Steve, was a pitcher and catcher in the minor leagues from 1979-1981.

5. Dave Stieb wrote an autobiography called *Tomorrow I'll Be Perfect*, which was released in 1986.

6. Four times in five years, Stieb reached the ninth inning with no-hitters. Three times in 12 months, he actually reached the last out of a no-hitter. Each time he missed out on finishing the bid. He had one no-hitter in his career and no perfect games. He threw four one-hitters before recording his no-hit bid.

7. Dave Stieb won a World Series with the Blue Jays in 1992.

He pitched for the White Sox the following season when the Blue Jays won their second World Series championship.

8. "He (Dave Stieb) isn't a Nolan Ryan, who overpowers you. But he throws two outstanding fastballs, one that sinks and one he throws by batters up. He has that awesome slider, a curveball, and a change-up, throws them all for strikes and isn't afraid to throw any of them at any time." — Sportswriter Peter Gammons in *The Sporting News* (June 13, 1983)

9. Dave Stieb was the first Blue Jays pitcher to be added to the Level of Excellence.

10. Stieb became interested in real estate through his agent in the 1980s, which is why he now buys and sells residential properties.

CONCLUSION

Learn anything new? Now you truly are the ultimate Blue Jays fan! Not only did you learn about the Blue Jays of the modern era, but you also expanded your knowledge back to the days of back-to-back World Series championships.

You learned about the Blue Jays' origins and their history. You learned about the history of their uniforms and jersey numbers, you identified some famous quotes, and read some of the craziest nicknames of all time. You learned more about the late, great Roy "Doc" Halladay and the impact he left, not only on the game of baseball, but on the world as a whole. You learned more about Robbie Alomar and Dave Stieb. You were amazed by Blue Jays stats and recalled some of the most famous Blue Jays trades and drafts/draft picks of all time. You broke down your knowledge by outfielders, infielders, pitchers, and catchers. You looked back on the Blue Jays' championships and playoff feats and the awards that came before, after, and during them. You also learned about the Blue Jays' fiercest rivalries both inside and outside their division.

Every team in MLB has a storied history, but the Blue Jays have one of the most memorable of all. They won back-to-back World Series championships with the backing of their devoted fans. Being the ultimate Blue Jays fan takes knowledge and a whole lot of patience, which you tested with this book. Whether you knew every answer or were stumped by several questions, you learned some of the most interesting history that the game of baseball has to offer.

The history of the Blue Jays represents what we all love about the game of baseball. The heart, the determination, the tough times, and the unexpected moments, plus the players who inspire us and encourage us to do our best because, even if you get knocked down, there is always another game and another day.

With players like Vladimir Guerrero Jr., Cavan Biggio, Bo Bichette, and Travis Shaw, the future for the Blue Jays continues to look bright. You can't have an all MLB-sons infield and not have some success, right?! There is no doubt that this franchise will continue to be one of the most competitive teams in Major League Baseball year after year.

It's a new decade, which means there is a clean slate, ready to continue writing the history of the Toronto Blue Jays. The ultimate Blue Jays fan cannot wait to see what's to come for their beloved team.

Made in United States
North Haven, CT
29 October 2022

26058289R00087